VOL **16** POL-RAD
1319–1406

FUNK & WAGNALLS **new**
ENCYCLOPEDIA
OF SCIENCE

FUNK & WAGNALLS, INC.

HOW TO USE FUNK & WAGNALLS NEW ENCYCLOPEDIA OF SCIENCE

Volumes 1 through 21 have information printed on the front covers, spine, and title pages that make it easy to find the articles you want to read.

- Volume numbers are printed in all three places in Volumes 1 through 21.
- Letter breaks — $\frac{COL}{DIA}$ — are printed in all three places in Volumes 1 through 21. The letters above the line are the first three letters of the first article title in the volume. The letters below the line are the first three letters of the last article title in the volume.
- Page breaks — $\frac{351}{438}$ — are printed on the spines and title pages of Volumes 1 through 21. They provide the page numbers of the first and last text pages in the volume.

Articles are arranged alphabetically by title in Volumes 1 through 21. Most titles are printed in **BOLD-FACE CAPITAL** letters. Some titles are printed in even larger letters.

- Some titles are not article titles, but refer you to the actual article title. Within articles you will find *See* or *See also* other article names for further information. All of these references to other articles are called cross-references.
- Most article titles are followed by a phonetic pronunciation. Use the Pronunciation Guide on page vi of Volume 1 to learn the correct pronunciation of the article title.
- At the end of most articles are two sets of initials. The first set identifies the person who wrote the article. The second set identifies the special consultant who checked the article for accuracy. All of these people are listed by their initials and full names and position on pages v and vi of Volume 1.
- ◣ This symbol at the end of an article indicates that there is a project based on the subject of the article in the Projects, Bibliography & Index volume. The project is found under its article title, and all of the project article titles are arranged alphabetically on pages 1 through 64 of the Projects, Bibliography & Index volume.

The Projects, Bibliography & Index Volume contains three sections. Each is an essential part of the encyclopedia.

- Projects based on articles in the encyclopedia are found in the first section. Each is both entertaining and educational. Each is designed for use by a student and for parental participation if desired.
- Bibliography reading lists in the second section list books under general scientific categories that are also titles of major articles. Each book listed is marked with either a YA (Young Adult) or J (Juvenile) reading level indicator. YA generally applies to readers at the junior high level or higher. J applies to readers at grade levels below junior high school.
- Index entries for all article titles plus many subjects that are not article titles are found in the third section. Instructions on using the Index are found at the start of the Index section in the Projects, Bibliography & Index volume.

POLONIUM (pə lō′ nē əm) Polonium (Po) is a radioactive metallic element. Its atomic number is 84. It melts at 254°C [489°F] and boils at 962°C [1,764°F]. Its relative density is 9.3.

Polonium was discovered in 1898 by the French chemists Marie and Pierre Curie. (*See* CURIE FAMILY.] This element is found in ores of uranium, but it is a very rare metal in nature. Most polonium is made artificially—not by nature—by bombarding bismuth with neutrons. Polonium has more isotopes, 27, than any other element. (*See* ISOTOPE.) The longest-lasting isotope is polonium-209. Half of it decays in 103 years. Polonium compounds are used, mixed with the metal beryllium, as a source of neutrons. *See also* RADIOACTIVITY.   M.E./J.R.W.

POLYESTER (päl′ ē es′ tər) Polyesters are a group of synthetic fibers and resins. (*See* FIBER.) Polyester fiber does not stretch or wrinkle. It is widely used in materials for dresses and suits. If polyester is heated and pressed at the same time, it forms a permanent crease, or fold. It is not affected by sunlight, and is a good material for curtains. Polyester fiber is made by reacting two compounds together: ethylene glycol and terephthalic acid. Ethylene glycol is an alcohol and terephthalic acid is an organic acid. Alcohols and organic acids react together to make compounds called esters. (*See* ESTER.) When ethylene glycol and terephthalic acid react together, a polymer is formed. (*See* POLYMERIZATION.) This polymer is called polyester. It can be melted and passed through a spinneret. A spinneret contains very small holes and the polyester is drawn out into long threads. (*See* EXTRUSION.) If different alcohols and acids are used, different kinds of polyesters are made. With some of these polyesters, the molecules can be cross-linked. This means that the atoms in different molecules form bonds. In this way the chain molecules join up and a resin is made. (*See* RESIN.) Polyester

resins are used in fiberglass. Fiberglass is used to make strong, rigid structures such as hulls of boats and automobile bodies. (*See* FIBERGLASS.) *See also* PLASTIC.   M.E./J.D.

POLYETHYLENE (päl′ ē eth′ ə lēn′) Polyethylene is probably the best known of all plastics. Plastic bags for wrapping food and other articles are made from polyethylene film. This plastic is also used for making buckets, washing bowls, and ''squeeze'' bottles for liquid detergents. There is also a heavier, more rigid type of polyethylene. It is used for bottles that contain liquid bleaches and for buckets and bowls that must withstand boiling water. These two types of polyethylene are called low-density and high-density polyethylene. They are made by polymerizing the gas ethylene. In polymerization, molecules of ethylene are joined together to form long molecules. (*See* POLYMERIZATION.) Low-density polyethylene is made by polymerizing ethylene at about 200°C [392°F] and at very high pressure, usually more than a thousand times atmospheric pressure. High-density polyethylene is made at the fairly low temperature of about 70°C [158°F] in the presence of a catalyst. The catalyst speeds up the rate of the reaction. (*See* CATALYST.) The pressure is only a little more than atmospheric pressure.

High-density polyethylene thread, after being extruded, is drawn through a hot water bath to harden the fiber. The thread can then be woven into tough fabrics.

These bottles are made from a high-density polyethylene. The plastic can be molded into any shape and is used for packaging material, pipes, electrical insulation, and plastic wrap and bags.

Courtesy of Union Carbide

The two types of polyethylene are different because their molecules have different structures. Low-density polyethylene has short-chain molecules with many branches. It is soft and non-crystalline. High-density polyethylene has longer-chain molecules with few branches. Its crystalline structure causes it to be hard and rigid. *See also* PLASTIC.

M.E./J.M.

POLYGON AND POLYHEDRON A polygon (päl′ i gän′) is any flat shape that has straight edges. The simplest polygon is a triangle. A triangle has three straight edges. A polygon with four straight edges is called a quadrilateral. A square is a special quadrilateral; all of its sides are the same length. A polygon with five edges is called a pentagon. A hexagon is a polygon with six sides and an octagon has eight sides.

If all the sides are the same length, the polygon is called a regular polygon. A square is a regular polygon. Certain polygons can be fitted together exactly, not leaving any spaces. This is called tesselation. Examples of tesselation can be seen in tile patterns. The only regular polygons that tesselate are the triangle, the square, and the hexagon.

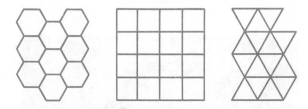

Semi-regular tesselations can also be made. These use more than one regular polygon. They still have no spaces in them.

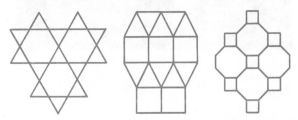

A polyhedron (päl' i hē' drən) is the solid (three-dimensional) equivalent of a polygon. Its faces are all flat and are polygons. If the faces are regular polygons, the polyhedron is called a regular polyhedron. A common example is the cube. Its faces are all squares. There are five regular polyhedra (the plural of polyhedron). Three have triangular faces—the tetrahedron (four faces), the octahedron (eight faces), and the icosahedron (20 faces). The other two are the cube and the dodecahedron. The dodecahedron has 20 faces, each of which is a pentagon.

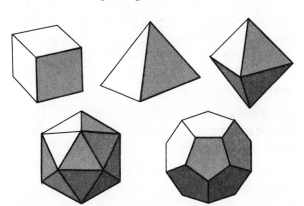

A polyhedron can be made by drawing the faces on a flat surface. The faces have to be drawn so that they join in the right way. The figure can then be cut out and folded to make a polyhedron.

 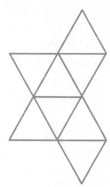

An interesting relationship exists between the faces, vertices, and edges of a polyhedron. Vertices are the points on the polyhedron. If the number of faces is F, the number of vertices V, and the number of edges E, then

$$F + V = E + 2.$$

For example, a cube has 6 faces and 8 vertices, and this makes 14. A cube has 12 edges and 12 + 2 is also 14. This law holds for all polyhedra. M.E./S.P.A.

POLYMERIZATION (pə lim' e rə zā' shən) Polymerization is a type of chemical reaction in which small molecules link up to form large molecules. The large molecules are called polymers. Each small molecule is called a monomer. Usually the polymer is a chainlike molecule. Polymers can be either natural or synthetic. Natural polymers include proteins, cellulose, and starch. They are found in the bodies of plants and animals. Synthetic (not found in nature) polymers include plastics and synthetic resins.

Polymers are usually compounds of carbon because molecules containing carbon are able to link together to form long chains. An important example of a polymer is polyethylene. (*See* POLYETHYLENE.) The monomer for polyethylene is the gas ethylene. Its formula is written as

$$CH_2{=}CH_2.$$

The two carbon atoms are held together by two bonds called a double bond. (*See* CHEMICAL BOND.) During polymerization, these double bonds split open and join onto carbon atoms in other molecules. In this way a long chain is formed:

$$...{-}CH_2{-}CH_2{-}CH_2{-}CH_2{-}CH_2{-}CH_2{-}...$$

Polymerization needs either high temperature and pressure, or a catalyst. (*See* CATALYST.)

There is one group of polymers that does not have carbon atoms linked together. These are the synthetic silicone rubbers. (*See* SILICONES.) In these molecules, silicon atoms are linked together. Their formula is $RXSi{=}O$. Si is silicon and O is oxygen. R and X stand for chemical groups that have carbon. They join up to form the polymer:

$$
\begin{array}{ccccc}
X & X & X & X & X \\
| & | & | & | & | \\
\end{array}
$$
$$...{-}Si{-}O{-}Si{-}O{-}Si{-}O{-}Si{-}O{-}Si{-}O{-}...$$
$$
\begin{array}{ccccc}
| & | & | & | & | \\
R & R & R & R & R \\
\end{array}
$$

M.E./J.D.

POLYMORPHISM (päl' i mòr' fiz' əm) Polymorphism is the existence of three or more distinct forms of a single species of plant or animal. The best examples are the social insects such as bees, ants, and termites. Each community contains queens, workers, and drones. Polymorphism also occurs among other insects, bacteria, jellyfish, molds, and protozoans. The differences in polymorphism may be the result of genetic or environmental factors, or both.

Dimorphism is a type of polymorphism in which there are only two distinct forms. The most common example is sexual dimorphism in which the male and the female of a species are markedly different in appearance. Different breeds or races of any one species of plant or animal are not considered to be examples of polymorphism. *See also* ANT; BEE; TERMITE.

A.J.C./C.R.N.

The bright-colored pochard drake, together with a dun-colored duck, is an example of color dimorphism. This is one kind of polymorphism.

POLYP (päl' əp) Animals belonging to the phylum Cnidaria have two body shapes. One is the polyp. Polyps are shaped like a vase, with an opening at the top. Food goes into, and waste products leave by this opening, or mouth. The mouth is surrounded by tentacles having nematocysts. A nematocyst is a tiny product of a cell which has a thread that can be thrown out in order to sting. The nematocyst is used for protection and for capturing prey (something that is to be killed for food). Adult sea anemones, corals, and hydra are polyps.

The other body shape that members of the phylum Cnidaria have is called a medusa. This shape is like that of a polyp turned upside down and shortened. *See also* CNIDARIA; CORAL; HYDRA; SEA ANEMONE. J.J.A./C.S.H.

POLYSTYRENE (päl' i stīər' ēn') Polystyrene is a common plastic in the home. Plastic measuring cups and some clear kitchenware are made from it. Polystyrene can be mixed with artificial rubber to make a substance called high-impact polystyrene. It is used in lining refrigerators. Another type of polystyrene is called expanded polystyrene. This material has many tiny air bubbles trapped inside it and is very light. It is used for packaging and for insulation. Many types of ceiling tiles are made of polystyrene.

Styrene is made from two compounds: ethylene (C_2H_4) and benzene (C_6H_6). In the presence of a catalyst, they react to form the compound ethyl benzene ($C_2H_5 \cdot C_6H_5$). (*See* CATALYST.) The ethyl benzene is then turned into styrene ($CH_2 = CH \cdot C_6H_5$). Molecules of styrene are joined together to form long chains. These long-chain molecules are called polystyrene. The process is called polymerization. (*See* POLYMERIZATION.) *See also* PLASTIC. M.E./J.M.

POLYURETHANE (päl′ ē yùr′ ə thän′) Polyurethane is a name given to a group of plastics. There are two main types of polyurethane. One type is a light, stretchable foam. It is used in clothing and upholstery materials. The other type is a hard foam. It can be shaped to make chairs and is also used for insulating buildings. *See also* PLASTIC. M.E./J.D.

POME (pōm′) A pome is a fruit that has a leathery, seed-containing core which grows from the ovary, or ovaries, of a flower. The part of the fruit that is fleshlike and can be eaten grows from the receptacle. (*See* FLOWER.) Members of the rose family, such as apples, pears, and hawthorns, are examples of pomes. *See also* FRUIT; ROSE FAMILY. A.J.C./M.H.S.

POMEGRANATE (päm′ ə gran′ ət) The pomegranate is the fruit of a deciduous tree (a tree whose leaves fall off at certain times) native to warmer areas of Europe and Asia. This tree (*Punica granatum*) grows to a height of 6 m [20 ft]. It has simple, sword-shaped leaves that are arranged in opposite pairs. (*See* LEAF.) The flowers have a tube-shaped calyx

and five to seven scarlet red petals that hang over each other. (*See* FLOWER.) The flowers grow in the axils or at the ends of stems. The fruit is a large berry with a hard rind and many seeds. The pulp, which is fleshlike and can be eaten, is usually golden red in color. *See also* FRUIT. A.J.C./F.W.S.

A young pomegranate fruit is pictured ripening in the sun.

PONDWEED (pän′ dwēd′) Pondweed is a family that includes five genera and 101 species of monocotyledonous plants that live in water. (*See* AQUATIC PLANT; MONOCOTYLE-DON.) All but four species belong to genus *Potamogeton*. The pondweeds usually live in freshwater ponds or in slow-moving streams. They have roots which go into the soil beneath the pond. The flowers are very tiny and grow above the top of the water, either singly or in spikes.

Water surfaces can become covered with pondweed.

Many types of pondweeds have small, thin leaves, all of which are underneath the surface. Some other kinds also have large, flat leaves which float on the top of the water. In nature, pondweeds serve as food for water birds and give surface cover and oxygen to fish. Pondweeds are often grown in aquariums to give oxygen to the fish.

A.J.C./M.H.S.

POPLAR (päp′ lər) The poplars are deciduous trees that belong to genus *Populus* of the willow family. (*See* DECIDUOUS TREE.) There are four species found in North America, although only the balsam poplar grows naturally in North America. Poplars grow to heights of 30 m [100 ft]. The leaves are alternate, simple and tear-shaped with toothed margins. (*See* LEAF.) The flowers hang in red or yellow catkins. (*See* CATKIN.) *See also* WILLOW FAMILY.

S.R.G./M.H.S.

A line of Lombardy poplar trees is shown above.

POPPY FAMILY The poppy (päp′ ē) family includes 25 genera with about 200 species of dicotyledonous plants, most of which are herbaceous. They have alternate leaves and brightly colored flowers. The flowers have two or three sepals, and twice as many petals. They usually have many stamens around one or two pistils. (*See* FLOWER.) The seeds grow in capsules (cases around the seeds of a plant) which open in dry weather after the seeds are grown. (*See* DISPERSION OF PLANTS.) These capsules also hold a poisonous, milky sap. (*See* ALKALOID.)

The most popular decorative poppy is the Oriental poppy (*Papaver orientale*). It is grown in temperate mild climate and subtropical areas for its large, reddish flowers. The most important member of the poppy family is the opium poppy (*Papaver somniferum*). It reaches a height of 1 to 5 m [3.3 to 16.5 ft] and has white flowers. The sap from capsules that are not fully grown is used as a drug itself, or can be made into narcotics such as heroin, morphine, and codeine. (*See* NARCOTIC.) It takes the sap from 100,000 capsules to produce 10 kg [22 lb] of opium. A.J.C./M.H.S.

Poppies are colorful weeds that spread quickly because of their efficient method of dispersing their seeds.

PORBEAGLE (pȯr′ bē′ gəl) The porbeagle is a large, voracious (having a huge appetite) shark of the genus *Lamna*. It grows 4 m [12 ft] long and lives in the North Atlantic and North Pacific Oceans. The porbeagle has a sharply pointed snout and a thick—almost rectangular—body that tapers sharply at the tail end. The first dorsal fin is very large and upright. The second dorsal and anal fins are very small.

The porbeagle and its close relative, the mako, are aggressive fish. They have been known to attack small boats at sea. Porbeagles rarely go into coastal waters. They feed on mackerel and other fish. Porbeagles are also known as mackerel sharks.   W.R.P./E.C.M.

PORCUPINE (pȯr′ kyə pīn′) The porcupine is a large rodent known for its strong, stiff quills. The quills are modified hairs that the porcupine uses to defend itself. Contrary to popular belief, porcupines cannot throw out quills from their bodies. They are not agressive animals. An attacker usually tries to grab the porcupine and gets a mouthful of quills.

There are two main groups of porcupines: Old World (family Hystricidae) and New World (family Erethizontidae). The Old World porcupines range throughout southern Europe, south Asia, Africa, and Indonesia. They feed mainly on bark, fruit, and vegetable matter. They usually live in tunnels. The largest Old World porcupine is the African crested porcupine (*Hystrix cristata*). When provoked, this porcupine shakes its quills in warning, making a rattling sound. As a last resort, it attempts to protect itself with its quills.

The only New World porcupine found in North America is the North American porcupine (*Erethizon dorsatum*). This porcupine is about 90 cm [3 ft] long and weighs about 9 kg [20 lb]. Its yellow-white quills are about 5 to 8 cm [2 to 3 in] long. It rams its enemies with its tail, placing quills into the attacker. The quills easily come off of the porcupine. The female gives birth to one baby in the spring. The solitary North American por-

cupine lives in trees and eats bark and green vegetables. *See also* RODENT.   J.M.C./J.J.M.

A porcupine of the Old World family is shown.

PORPOISE (pȯr′ pəs) The porpoise is a small member of the order of whales, Cetacea. It is often confused with the dolphin. There are two important differences between porpoises and dolphins. The porpoise has ''spoon-shaped'' teeth and a snout that does not form a beak. The dolphin has ''cone-shaped'' teeth and a snout that is shaped like a beak.

The common porpoise (*Phocaena phocaena*) has a gray back and white underside. It grows to about 1.5 m [5 ft] long, and may weigh up to 45 kg [100 lb]. The common porpoise is found along the coasts of North America, South America, Europe, Africa, and Asia. Common porpoises travel in small groups of two to five animals. Porpoises feed on herring, mackerel, other fish, crustaceans, and squids.   J.J.A./J.J.M.

A porpoise leaps high from the water. Porpoises are often seen chasing shoals of flying fish.

PORTLAND CEMENT (pōrt′ lənd si ment′) Portland cement is a type of cement that hardens under water. Its main use is in the making of concrete.

Portland cement is made up of 60 percent lime, 25 percent silica, 10 percent alumina, and small amounts of gypsum and iron oxide. These materials undergo a complicated process of crushing, grinding, burning, and fine grinding. The gypsum controls the hardening of the cement. The finished product is strong and lasts for a long time. The United States leads the world in the making of Portland cement.

Portland cement was invented by Joseph Aspdin, an English bricklayer, in 1824. He named his invention Portland cement because it was the same color as a type of limestone found on the Isle of Portland in Great Britain. In 1917, a standard recipe for Portland cement was established. *See also* CEMENT AND CONCRETE.   J.M.C./R.W.L.

PORTUGUESE MAN-OF-WAR (pōr′ chə gēz′ man′ əv wōr′) The Portuguese man-of-war is a jellyfish that floats on the surface of tropical seas and on the Gulf Stream of the North Atlantic Ocean. It is not really a single animal, but rather a group of animals, or polyps, attached to a hollow float that looks like a bladder. (*See* POLYP.) The Portuguese man-of-war belongs to the phylum Coelenterata.

The full-grown float is about 20 cm [8 in] long. It is filled with gas that allows it to float. Long, stringlike filaments, called tentacles, hang down from the float. These tentacles act as arms and are used to take prey (something that is to be killed for food), such as a small fish. The tentacles hold a poison that seems to paralyze a fish when the tentacles touch it. The Portuguese man-of-war is also dangerous to humans. Swimmers touching them get painful lumps or even deadly shock.

The individual polyps and medusae make up what is called a colony. Each animal has a separate job to do. Some of them reproduce their kind. Others find food, while still others defend the colony. *See also* HYDRA.

W.R.P./C.S.H.

This photo of a Portuguese man-of-war shows the gas-filled float which drifts with the wind, and the hanging colony of polyps, including those with tentacles bearing dangerous stinging cells.

POTASSIUM (pə tas′ ē əm) Potassium (K) is a soft silvery metallic element. It is one of the alkali group of elements. (*See* ALKALI METAL.) Its atomic number is 19 and its atomic weight is 39.102. Potassium melts at 63°C [146°F] and boils at 774°C [1,425°F]. It is lighter than water and its relative density is 0.86.

Potassium was discovered in 1807 by the British scientist Sir Humphry Davy. Salts of potassium are found in many different minerals. It is taken out of minerals by a process called electrolysis. (*See* ELECTROLYSIS.) Potassium is necessary to many forms of life. Nerves need potassium ions to send messages. (*See* NERVOUS SYSTEM.) It is also an important food for plants and many fertilizers have potassium in them.

Potassium is one of the most reactive of all elements. It combines very quickly with the oxygen in the air and has to be stored under oil. It bursts into flame when placed in water. Potassium itself has few uses, but many of its compounds are very important. Potassium bromide and iodide are used in medicine and photography. Potassium chlorate is used to make fireworks and matches. Potassium hydroxide, which is also known as caustic potash, is used in making soap and textiles.

M.E./J.R.W.

POTATO (pə tāt′ ō) The potato is a plant of the nightshade family. It has about 1,000 close relatives in the genus *Solanum*. The potato plant has alternate leaves and flowers with five petals and five stamens forming a cone at the center. The plant stores starch in a swollen, underground stem called a tuber. This is the common vegetable. The tuber is either round or oval and has a thin brown or red skin. The flesh is white.

The tuber, or potato, is about 80 percent water and 20 percent solid matter. About 85 percent of the potato is starch. About 10 percent of the potato is protein. The potato also contains the vitamins thiamine, riboflavin, niacin, ascorbic acid, and a small amount of vitamin A. Many other elements are also present including calcium, iron, magnesium, phosphorous, potassium, and sodium. A potato is not especially fattening, although many people believe it is. A medium-sized new potato contains about 70 calories.

About 11 billion bushels of potatoes are grown throughout the world each year. They are widely used as a table food and may be baked, boiled, or fried. Manufacturers use billions of bushels each year to make potato chips and frozen french-fried potatoes. Many schools and large institutions use dehydrated (the water has been taken out) potato powder to make mashed or whipped potatoes. This is done by adding water or milk when cooking. Millions of bushels of potatoes are used each year to make alcohol, flour, and starch.

The Soviet Union, with a yearly production of 2 billion bushels, is the leading grower of potatoes in the world. China and Poland are the next largest growers. The United States grows more than 500 million bushels a year. Idaho is the leading potato-growing state. Washington, Oregon, Maine, and California also grow large crops.

The potato was first grown in South America. Spanish explorers took the potato with them on a return trip to Europe around 1550. In Ireland, potatoes grew so well that they became the country's main food. Potatoes were introduced into the United States in 1719 by Irish immigrants who settled in Londonderry, New Hampshire. The common white potato then became known as the Irish potato. *See also* BURBANK, LUTHER; NIGHTSHADE FAMILY.

W.R.P./F.W.S.

POTENTIAL (pə ten′ chəl) Potential is a name used to describe several different quantities used in physics. In order to lift a body through a certain distance, work has to be done on it. Work is a form of energy. When you lift a body, energy is transferred from you to the body. You lose energy because you are doing work. The body gains energy because it is being lifted. When the body has been lifted, it has energy because of its position. This energy is called potential energy. When the body falls, this energy is charged into energy of movement, called kinetic energy. (*See* ENERGY.)

A certain point has potential if a body has potential energy when placed at that point. For example, a body near or on the earth's surface has gravitational potential energy because it is in the earth's gravitational field.

(*See* FIELD.) Any object placed in this field is pulled downward by gravity.

In the same way, an electric charge makes an electric field in the area around it. This electric field attracts or repels other charges. (If two charges have the same sign, either both positive or both negative, they repel each other— they are not attracted to each other. If they have opposite signs, such as a negative charge and a positive charge, they attract each other.) The electric potential at any point in this electric field is a specific description that tells how much potential energy stored in the field may be associated with each point. The difference in potential between two points in an electric field is called the potential difference. This is equal to the work that must be done in moving a charge of +1 coulomb from one point to the other. Another name for potential difference is voltage. (*See* COULOMB; VOLTAGE.) Electric potential is measured in units of joules per coulomb, also called volts. When we say that a battery has 6 volts, this means that 6 joules of energy are required to move a charge of 1 coulomb from one battery terminal to the other.

M.E./R.W.L.

POTHOLE (pät′ hōl′) A pothole is a hole worn in rock by the action of water. Potholes are often found in the beds of rivers. They are also found at the bottom of waterfalls where loose gravel and large stones are stirred by the whirling water. The grinding action of the gravel and stones wears holes in the hardest rocks. Potholes can be as large as 7 m [20 ft] across and 17 m [50 ft] deep.

Other potholes are found in limestone formations. They are sometimes called sink holes or swallow holes. Rainwater soaks up carbon dioxide from the atmosphere and makes weak carbonic acid. This mixture reacts with the limestone to create the potholes.

Holes in asphalt-paved roads are also called potholes. They are found mostly in northern, mild–climate regions where ex-

treme temperature changes cause the pavement to break up.   W.R.P./W.R.S.

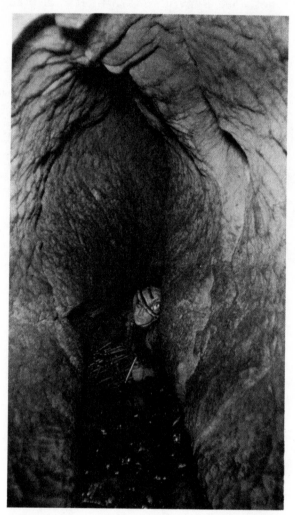

Potholers often encounter deep water in their exploration of potholes and caves.

POULTRY (pōl′ tre) Poultry is the name for the various kinds of birds raised for their meat or eggs. Chickens and turkeys are the most common types of poultry. Other kinds of poultry include ducks, geese, pheasants, pigeons, quail, and guinea fowl.

Chickens are the most common kind of poultry. Many different breeds of chicken exist today. They are divided into two main groups: those raised for their eggs and those raised for their meat. Laying hens are female chickens raised to produce eggs. They start

Many domestic poultry are reared on special farms. Domestic fowl, such as chickens, are often bred in this way. The Malayan jungle fowl and the mallard (shown in circles) are the wild ancestors of the domestic fowl and the farmyard duck, respectively.

laying eggs when they are about 22 weeks old. The birds are kept in long, low buildings called laying houses. One laying house may hold as many as 50,000 hens. Broilers or fryers are chickens raised only for their meat. Most broilers are raised indoors on a dirt or concrete floor covered with litter. The litter absorbs moisture to keep the birds clean. Broilers eat and drink from automatic feeders and water containers.

Turkeys need more space because they are larger than chickens. Most turkeys are raised outdoors in pens or fenced fields.

Poultry feed contains a mixture of ingredients that promotes fast growth or high egg production. Grains such as corn or wheat are mixed with protein supplements, such as soybean.

Diseases and parasites are a chief problem of poultry farms. To prevent disease among their poultry, farmers often vaccinate their birds, add drugs to the feed or drinking water, and try to keep their flocks clean.

Each person in the United States eats an average of about 25 kg [55 lb] of poultry each year. More than 75 percent of this meat comes from chickens, and about 15 percent from turkeys. The rest comes from ducks, pheasants, geese, and other fowl.

Besides being used for food, poultry also provides some by-products. The feathers of ducks and geese are sometimes used to stuff pillows and to insulate clothing. Poultry manure is used as fertilizer. Eggs, aside from their use as food, are used in making paint and other products.   J.J.A./F.W.S.

POUNDAL (paùn′ dl) The poundal is the unit of force in the foot-pound-second system of units. (*See* FORCE.) A force of one poundal accelerates a mass of one pound by one foot per second per second. A poundal is equal to

0.13825 newtons. A newton is the unit of force in the international system of units. (*See* NEWTON.) M.E./R.W.L.

POWDER METALLURGY (paùd′ ər met′ l ər′ jē) Powder metallurgy is the way in which articles are made from metal powders. By using powders, objects that are difficult to make can be made quickly and with little waste. Frequently, mixtures of different metals are used. Sometimes non-metallic substances are also added. Powder metallurgy also studies the ways of making powders.

There are several ways of making powders. The most widely used method starts with the metal oxide. The metal oxide, which is a powder, is reduced to the metal by a reducing agent. This reaction is called a reduction reaction. (*See* OXIDATION AND REDUCTION.) This reaction leaves the metal behind. It is in powder form because the oxide was in powder form. Another method is called atomization. In this method, a thin stream of molten metal is broken down by a blast of air.

The first stage in making an article is to mix the powder with a lubricant. (*See* FRICTION.) The lubricant helps the powder to pack tighter. The powder is then forced by pressure into a mold or die. The pressure can be as much as 50 tons per square inch [7000 kg per sq cm]. The pressed powder is called a compact. It is then heated in a furnace to three fourths of the melting point of the metal. This process is called sintering. Sometimes the metal has many tiny pores or holes. They can be removed by sintering twice. Another way of removing the pores is to add a small amount of another metal. This metal has a lower melting point than the main metal. It melts during sintering and fills up the pores. This is called infiltration.

Sometimes, however, the pores are necessary. For example, porous metal is used for filters. Porous bronze can be made to soak up oil. It is used as a self-lubricating material for bearings. It slowly releases the oil which then acts as a lubricant. M.E./A.D.

POWER (paù′ ər) In physics, power is the rate of doing work. For example, if you lift a certain mass through a certain distance, then you do work. The faster you lift it, the more power you use. In the international system of units, work is measured in units called joules. Therefore, power is measured in joules per second, or watts. In the foot-pound-second system, the unit of power is called the horsepower. One horsepower is equal to 550 foot-pounds per second. M.E./J.T.

PRAIRIE DOG (prer′ ē dȯg′) The prairie dog is a burrowing rodent belonging to the squirrel family Sciuridae. It has its name because of its barking call. The prairie dog inhabits the open plains and plateaus of North America from Canada to Mexico.

The prairie dog grows to about 30 cm [1 ft] long, not including its short, flat tail. The animal has coarse gray and brown fur. It is stout and has short legs.

The prairie dog is a sociable animal—it lives in a community with other prairie dogs. The animal builds its burrow by digging about 3.7 m [12 ft] underground. At the bottom of the tunnel, several different chambers may be hollowed out—one for sleeping, one for storing food, and so on. The prairie dog makes a

Prairie dogs look rather like squirrels but live in burrows. They have short gray and brown fur, and build their burrows by digging about 3.7 m [12 ft] underground and then hollowing out several different chambers.

mound of earth at the entrance to the hole. This mound keeps water from entering the hole. These homes give the prairie dogs protection from enemies such as coyotes, badgers, weasels, and eagles.

Prairie dogs feed on grass and other plants. They especially like alfalfa and grain. Prairie dogs are serious pests to farmers. Not only do these animals eat crops, but a horse or cow that steps into a prairie dog's home could break a leg. To reduce their numbers, millions of prairie dogs have been killed by poisoned food and poison gases. J.J.A./J.J.M.

PRASEODYMIUM (prā′ zē ō dim′ ē əm) Praseodymium (Pr) is a soft, silvery metallic element. Is is one of the rare earth group of metals. (*See* RARE EARTH ELEMENT.) Its atomic number is 59 and its atomic weight is 140.908. Praseodymium melts at 931°C [1,708°F] and boils at 3,512°C [6,354°F].

Praseodymium was discovered by the Austrian chemist Karl Auer von Welsbach in 1885. It is found in minerals such as monazite with other rare earth metals. Salts of praseodymium are used for coloring glass. They produce a bright yellow color.

M.E./J.R.W.

PRAWN (prȯn′) A prawn is any of various crustaceans with narrow, shrimplike bodies and five pairs of walking legs. The bodies are somewhat flattened from side to side. Some types of prawns live in coastal waters, mainly where the bottom is sandy. Others live in the open sea, often at great depths, where it is very dark. Some species have luminous spots. Most prawns are scavengers and eat dead plants and animals.

Some tropical and deep sea prawns are about 30 cm [1 ft] long. Most species are much smaller. The common prawn (*Palaemon serratus*) is about 7.5 to 10 cm [3 to 4 in] long. It can be distinguished from the commercial shrimps by the lack of claws on the third set of legs. *See also* SHRIMP.

J.J.A./C.S.H.

PRECAMBRIAN ROCK (prē kam′ brē ən räk′) Precambrian rock is rock that formed at least 570 million years ago, during Precambrian times. Although some Precambrian rocks can still be seen above the surface, most of them are covered by accumulations of sediment. Among the most important Precambrian rocks are those that compose the continental shields. The continental shields acted as cores around which the continents formed.

Fossils of algae, dating from the Archeozoic era, have been discovered in Precambrian rock. The algae lived about 3.5 billion years ago, thus making them the oldest proof of life on earth. The oldest known rocks are from Greenland. They date back about 3.8 billion years. *See also* DATING; EARTH; PRECAMBRIAN TIME. J.M.C./W.R.S.

PRECAMBRIAN TIME (prē kam′ brē ən tīm′) Precambrian time is the name that geologists have given to the earliest division of the earth's geological time scale. Precambrian time began about 4.6 billion years ago, the same time that the earth's crust probably formed, and ended about 570 million years ago. Thus, Precambrian time includes approximately 80 percent of the earth's history.

Huge outcrops of Precambrian rock are found in many parts of the world. These outcrops, called continental shields, are most clear in Canada, Greenland, and Scandinavia. The continental shields acted as cores which the continents formed around. (*See* PRECAMBRIAN ROCK.) The climate of Precambrian time has not yet been decided, although most geologists agree that large glaciation (ice covering the land) happened at the end of the Precambrian time.

Precambrian time is often divided into three eras: Azoic era, Archeozoic era, and Proterozoic era. The Azoic era saw the formation of the earth. The atmosphere probably formed later on during the Azoic era. Evidence suggests that the earth's crust melted

Leander (facing left), a common prawn, is shown. A prawn is a crustacean with five pairs of walking legs. The common prawn has a third set of legs.

and hardened several times during this time. Proof of life during the Azoic era is completely missing.

The first forms of life came out during the Archeozoic era. Primitive algae and bacteria evolved. Fossils of these organisms have been found in rocks dating to this era. The heat, pressure, and chemical processes within the earth's crust caused the formation of such metamorphic rocks as marble and slate. Large bodies of granite also formed during the Archeozoic era. Volcanic activity was widespread.

Proterozoic rocks have large amounts of iron ore. A greater variety of life, including jellyfish, sponges, and worms, lived on the earth during the Proterozoic era. *See also* ARCHEOZOIC ERA; GEOLOGICAL TIME SCALE, PROTEROZOIC ERA.   J.M.C./W.R.S.

PRECESSION (prē sesh' ən) Precession is the comparatively slow gyration (movement around a point or axis) of a spinning body about another line intersecting it. When anything spins, it spins around an axis. The axis is a line through the object around which the object spins. For example, a spinning top spins around a line through its center. When the top is spinning fast, the axis is vertical: it points straight up and down. When the top slows down, the axis falls away from the vertical and develops a wobble. The axis now rotates about the vertical. This movement of the axis is called precession.

The earth provides another example of precession. The earth spins around an imaginary line that connects the North and South Pole. It completes one revolution every day. The sun and moon exert a force of gravity on the earth. This force causes the earth's axis to move slowly round in a circle. The Pole Star, or North Star, is the star that lies nearest to due

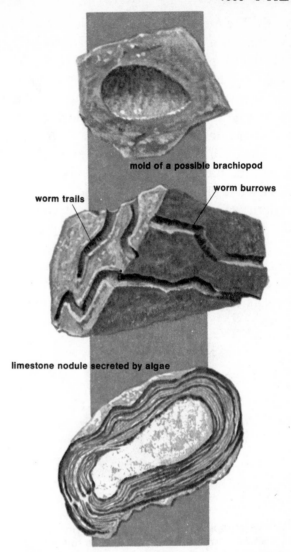

mold of a possible brachiopod

worm burrows

worm trails

limestone nodule secreted by algae

Traces of early Precambrian life from rock fossils are illustrated above.

The Beacon Hill Beds (above) are Precambrian rocks found in England. These kinds of rocks are also found in Africa, Australia, eastern Canada, northern Europe and the Soviet Union.

north. The present Pole Star is called Polaris. As the earth's axis precesses, Polaris will eventually move away from due North. Another star will then be nearest to due north and it will be taken as the Pole Star. In the same way, 14,000 years ago the Pole Star was the bright star Vega.

The earth's precession produces an effect called the precession of the equinoxes. The sun and the planets all lie in a plane called the ecliptic. (*See* ECLIPTIC.) This plane crosses the earth's equator at two opposite points. These points are called the equinoxes. Because the earth precesses, these equinoxes are slowly moving westwards. The equinoxes pass once round the ecliptic every 25,800 years. M.E./C.R.

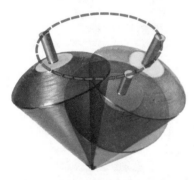

The axis of a spinning top (above) shows precession as it slows down. The path the handle follows is shown as a red dotted line.

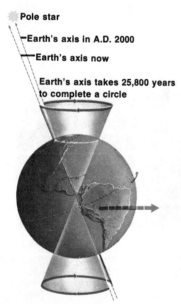

Pole star

Earth's axis in A.D. 2000

Earth's axis now

Earth's axis takes 25,800 years to complete a circle

The axis of the spinning globe describes a double cone as it precesses in the opposite direction to the spin of the earth. At present the earth's axis points almost to the Pole Star. In the year A.D. 2000, the earth's axis will point directly at the Pole Star.

PRECIOUS STONE AND GEM A precious stone (presh′ əs stōn′) is a mineral that occurs naturally in the rocks of the earth. (*See* MINERAL.) In general, a gem (jem′) is any mineral or stone used for jewelry and other decorative purposes. The word gem comes from the Latin word *gemma*, which means "bud." As a bud forms into a lovely flower, dull lumps of a mineral can be cut and polished into brilliant (sparkling) gems. Several different gems may come from the same mineral. For example, ruby and sapphire are both formed from the mineral corundum. (*See* CORUNDUM; RUBY; SAPPHIRE.)

Some gems do not come from minerals. For example, the pearl is a gem that is not a stone. The pearl is taken from a mollusk (a water-dwelling animal), usually an oyster. (*See* OYSTER; PEARL.) Amber, another substance used as a gem, is a hard substance formed from the resin of trees that grew millions of years ago. (*See* AMBER.) Coral, which is often used in necklaces, is made by tiny sea animals. (*See* CORAL.) Jet is fossilized coal.

Imitation stones are often made of a soft glass called paste, or strass. This glass is very clear and brilliant. Imitation gems made from this paste can be scratched easily. Many imitation gems are made from plastics.

Synthetic gems are made of the same material as natural gems, but they are made in the laboratory. For example, rubies and sapphires have been made by melting aluminum oxide in a flame from oxygen and hydrogen gases. It is hard to tell the difference between good quality synthetic gems and natural gems.

Qualities of precious stones There are various properties (features, characteristics) used to identify gem minerals. One is the shape of

Precious stones, such as diamonds, are used in all types of jewelry because of their brilliance. In many parts of the world diamonds are used in engagement rings (facing right), such as those pictured here. Diamonds are generally the most prized gems because they surpass all other stones in hardness and brilliance.

the crystals, which differs with each gem mineral. All crystals in any one mineral always have the same type of symmetry (the same size shape and position of parts). For example, diamonds crystallize in the isometric system. (*See* CRYSTAL.)

Color is an important factor in deciding the beauty and splendor of gems. Some very dark or cloudy precious stones depend entirely on color for their beauty. Transparent stones without much color may have beauty because they are able to reflect light. There are two types of color in precious stones. Essential color is the color of the mineral in its pure state (without impurities). Nonessential color comes from some impurity.

Another factor that determines the beauty of a precious stone is how it affects light that passes through it or is reflected from it. When light passes from air to a denser (thicker) substance, the speed of light is slowed down. The ratio of the speed of light in air to its speed in the stone is the gem's index (sign) of refraction. (*See* REFRACTION OF LIGHT.) Minerals with a high index of refraction sparkle and glitter. Minerals with a low index of refraction usually appear dull and have a low luster. The amount of refraction also varies with the color of the light that passes through the mineral. For example, blue rays are refracted more than yellow rays, and yellow rays more than red. Beams of white light passed through some stones become separated into various colored rays. This is called dispersion. (*See* DIAMOND; LIGHT.)

Cleavage is the tendency of some minerals to split along certain directions, producing an even surface. This surface is different from the surface that comes from a fracture. Each mineral has a certain cleavage direction, type of fracture, or both.

Experts also identify gem minerals by specific gravity. Specific gravity, or relative density, is a comparison of the weight of an equal amount of pure water. (*See* RELATIVE DENSITY.)

Hardness is an important quality of gem minerals. Few stones can serve as gems unless they will wear for a long time. However, some stones, such as opals, are fairly soft. (*See* HARDNESS.)

Cutting   The tools used for cutting depend on the hardness of the mineral. Proper cutting brings out the brilliance and color of stones. Also, flaws (imperfections) are removed. Transparent stones, such as diamonds, are usually faceted, that is, their surfaces are cut into a series of small square or triangular faces (sides) that reflect and refract light. Nontransparent stones, such as rubies (which are often flawed), are generally cut with a rounded surface. This is called cabochon cutting. After a mineral has been cut, it is polished.

Value of precious stones   Diamonds are generally the most prized gems because they surpass all others in hardness and brilliance. Besides hardness and brilliance, other factors determine the value of gems, such as color, rarity, and demand. For example, the value of sapphires depends on the quality of the blue color. Rubies are more valuable than sapphires because rubies are more rare. Certain emeralds, because of their demand, may be more valuable than some diamonds.

J.J.A./R.H.

PRECIPITATE (pri sip' ət ət) A precipitate is a substance separated from a solution or suspension by a chemical change.

When two solutions are mixed together, they sometimes react to form different substances. If one of the substances is insoluble (cannot be dissolved), then it forms a suspension of solid particles. This suspension is called a precipitate. For example, many metal hydroxides are insoluble. Suppose a solution of sodium hydroxide is mixed with a solution of copper sulfate. A blue precipitate of copper hydroxide is immediately formed. Precipitates can also be made by changing the temperature of a solution. The amount of a substance that can dissolve in a certain amount of water changes with the temperature. If the temperature is varied so that this amount decreases, then a precipitate may form. Usually the temperature has to be lowered to form a precipitate.

Most precipitates are made of many small particles. However, the precipitate may occur as flakes. This is called a flocculent precipitate. The precipitate may at other times be jellylike or gelatinous. *See also* SOLUTION AND SOLUBILITY.   M.E./A.D.

PRECIPITATION (pri sip′ ə tā′ shən) Precipitation is the descent (coming down) of liquid or solid water particles from clouds to the ground. Forms of precipitation include drizzle, rain, freezing rain, sleet, snow, and hail.

As air rises it cools and cannot hold as much water vapor (the gaseous state of a liquid substance). At a temperature known as the dew point, the water vapor condenses (concentrates) on tiny particles in the air, forming water droplets. These particles, called condensation nuclei, include dust particles and sea salt. (*See* CONDENSATION; DEW POINT.) The water droplets aggregate (collect) together, forming clouds or fog. If the water droplets become supercooled (remain liquid below the freezing point, 0°C [32°F]), the droplets combine, and may be heavy enough to fall to the ground as rain or snow. Most kinds of precipitation form in this way.

If precipitation is in the form of very small water droplets, it is called drizzle. The water droplets that make up drizzle have diameters ranging from 0.2 to 0.5 mm [.008 to .02 in]. The total amount of precipitation which comes from drizzle is often hardly worth noting.

Water droplets larger than those of drizzle are called rain. The maximum diameter of a raindrop is about 6 mm [.25 in]. The largest raindrops usually fall during heavy storms. Freezing rain happens when the raindrops fall through a layer of air colder than 0°C [32°F]. Freezing rain presents a danger to motorists and pedestrians alike because it coats everything with a thin glaze of ice.

Snow is frozen water that always remains in the solid state. It only falls when the temperature is near or below freezing. Snowfall is classified by the accumulated (collected) amount. Winter snowstorms are commonplace in many parts of the United States. (*See* SNOW.) Sleet is either mixed rain and snow or partially frozen ice particles. Hail is frozen precipitation that falls only from cumulonimbus (thunderhead) clouds during thunderstorms. *See also* CLOUD; HAIL; RAIN.
J.M.C./C.R.

PREGNANCY (preg′ nən sē) Pregnancy is the period of time that a woman carries a baby inside her body before giving birth. Pregnancy begins when a fertilized egg attaches itself to the lining of the uterus. (*See* FERTILIŒ ZATION; IMPLANTATION.) Except in rare cases, the egg is fertilized through sexual intercourse.

Pregnancy is also called gestation. For most women, gestation lasts about nine months. The females of nearly all other kinds of mammals also have a period of gestation. The length of this period varies among different animals. (*See* GESTATION PERIOD.)

In human pregnancy, the developing baby is called an embryo during the first two months of pregnancy. (*See* EMBRYO.) From this time until birth, the developing baby is called a fetus. In early pregnancy, certain structures form in the uterus. Such structures make it possible for the embryo to live within the mother's body. The placenta is one of the most important of these structures. By means of the placenta, food and oxygen pass from the mother's bloodstream to the embryo or fetus. (*See* PLACENTA.) After two months, the fetus, though only about 2.5 cm [1 in] in length, can move its head, mouth, arms, and legs.

During the fifth month, the mother can usually feel the fetus moving inside her, and the fetal heartbeat can be heard. In the sixth month, the fetus measures roughly 30 cm [1 ft] long, weighing about 0.5 to 0.7 kg [1 to 1.5 lb]. Most of the fetus's organs can function. During the final few months of pregnancy, the mother's bloodstream gives the fetus various immunities. These immunities help protect the baby from various diseases for a short period after birth.

As the embryo and then the fetus undergoes an enormous development through pregnancy, pregnancy also causes bodily and emotional changes in women. Menstruation stops, morning sickness (vomiting) may occur, weight is gained, and the breasts change. The bodily changes make it possible for the mother to nurse the baby after it is born. Such changes may make a woman feel happy or depressed. Pregnant women may have many moods.

To prevent harm to the embryo, doctors advise pregnant women not to smoke or take alcohol or certain drugs. Spontaneous abortion, also known as miscarriage, is an early ending of pregnancy by a natural or accidental cause. (*See* ABORTION.) Medical treatment throughout pregnancy can prevent many miscarriages from happening. *See also* REPRODUCTION; SEX. J.J.A./J.J.F.

PREHISTORY (prē his' tə rē) Prehistory is the time before human beings developed methods for writing about their lives. It includes all time before about 7,000 years ago in certain parts of the world, such as the Near East. In other regions, such as in parts of Africa, there have been no written records until as recently as a few hundred years.

The knowledge of prehistoric times that scientists have obtained is decided almost completely from the study of animal and human fossils, ancient tools and other evidence of human beings, and from the study of rocks. Geologists, anthropologists, and paleontologists all strive toward a fuller understanding of the prehistoric earth and its life forms. *See also* FOSSIL; GEOLOGICAL TIME SCALE; PALEONTOLOGY. J.M.C./S.O.

PRESSURE (presh' ər) Pressure is the force exerted by a body over the surface of another body.

Suppose that you are carrying a heavy parcel by its string. In a short while the string starts to cut into your hand. The weight is much easier to carry if the parcel is in a bag with a handle. Both the string and the handle exert a pressure on your hand. However the pressure of the string is much greater than the pressure of the handle. That is why the string quickly starts to hurt. Pressure is defined as force divided by the area over which it acts. In the two examples above, the force, or weight of the parcel, is the same in each case. But, because the string is thin, the area of contact with your hand is very small. This means that the pressure is very large. The handle covers a much greater area of your hand because it is wider. Therefore its pressure is much less.

Different substances react differently to pressure. When you press your hands against wood, the wood is not noticeably affected. However, when you press against clay, the clay distorts (changes shape). This is because the forces between the molecules in wood are strong. In clay, they are not strong enough to resist the pressure of your hand.

The forces between the molecules in a liquid are weaker than in a solid. Therefore, liquids are very easily distorted by pressure, and you can easily put your hand into a bowl of water. In a gas, the forces are weaker still and a gas can be compressed by pressure.

Gases and liquids are together known as fluids. The branch of physics that studies the pressures in fluids is called hydrostatics. (*See* FLUID MECHANICS.) At any point inside a fluid, the pressure is the same in all directions.

Shown at the left is the spacesuit that astronauts of the Apollo program wore. The backpack contained the astronaut's oxygen supply (including an emergency oxygen tank), the spacesuit cooling system, and a radio. The spacesuit itself was really two suits. The oversuit was padded to protect the astronaut from small bits of flying meteorites. The inner suit was made of rubber and was pressure-tight. The inner suit was cooled by water that circulated in plastic tubes. Although the spacesuit looked bulky, it was flexible enough to allow the astronaut adequate movement.

This is true for the air in the atmosphere. The column of air above us exerts a pressure on us. The pressure is about 101,600 newtons per square meter [14.7 pounds per square inch]. Over the area of your hand, this is equal to a weight of about 70 kg [150 lb]. This is the weight of a person. However the pressure acts in all directions. It acts on both sides of your hand and so it balances out.

A gas can be easily compressed because the forces between its molecules are very weak, and they can be easily forced together. Although the forces between the molecules are much stronger in liquids and solids, they, too, can be compressed, though the change in volume is very small. If the pressure on a gas is doubled, then the volume is roughly halved. This law is called Boyle's law. (*See* BOYLE'S LAW.) At very high pressures, the molecules in a gas are very close together and Boyle's law no longer applies.

M.E./J.T.

PRESSURE GAUGE (presh' ər gaj') A pressure gauge is an instrument that measures pressure. Such gauges are widely used in industry and scientific research. There are many different types of pressure gauges. For example, the manometer has a U-shaped tube containing a liquid. One end of the tube is connected to the pressurized system. The other end is left open. The pressure forces the liquid down one side of the tube and up the other. The difference in the two levels is used to calculate the pressure. (*See* MANOMETER.)

The Bourdon gauge is another common type of pressure gauge. It can measure fairly high pressures. It contains a C-shaped coil. The coil is a tube with thin walls. It is closed at one end. The open end is connected to the pressurized system. The pressure tries to straighten the tube out. This causes the free end of the coil to move which, in turn, moves a pointer on a dial. More sensitive gauges have a spiral-shaped tube.

There are also bellow-shaped gauges. The "bellows" are made out of a metal tube with corrugated (wavelike folds) walls. One end of the tube moves under pressure while the other end is kept still. The aneroid barometer works in a similar way. It is used for measuring the pressure of the atmosphere.

All these instruments measure pressure directly. However, they are not sensitive (capable of responding) enough for very low pressures. In this case some quantity is measured that varies with pressure. For example, the thermal conductivity or ionization of a substance may be measured.   M.E./R.W.L.

PRIESTLEY, JOSEPH (1733–1804) Joseph Priestley (prēst' lē) was an English chemist. He is best known for his discovery of the gas oxygen. Priestley was originally a preacher. He became involved with science after meeting the great American scientist and statesman Benjamin Franklin. Priestley investigated gases. He was the first person to dissolve the gas carbon dioxide in water. This is how soda water is made. He also investigated the gases hydrogen chloride and ammonia. In 1774 he made oxygen by heating the compound mercuric oxide.   M.E./D.G.F.

Joseph Priestley

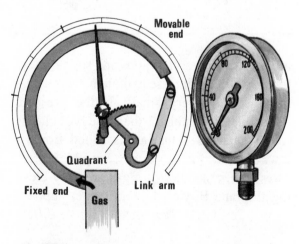

The Bourdon gauge is often used on steam boilers. When the pressure inside the boiler increases, the tube straightens out; and the needle on the dial moves up.

PRIMATE (prī' māt') Primates make up an order of mammals which includes human beings and more than 200 species of other animals that are like human beings. Except for human beings, most primates live in trees in tropical or subtropical areas. They have large, well-developed brains, and eyes that give them good vision. Most primates have hands with four fingers and an opposable thumb.

This illustration of different kinds of primates includes a tree shrew (1), which is often classified as a primitive primate. Primates are divided into two groups. Prosimians include the lemur (2) and the tarsier (3). Anthropoids include the uakari (4), a New World monkey; the Baboon (5) an Old World monkey; and the orangutan (6), an ape.

1

2

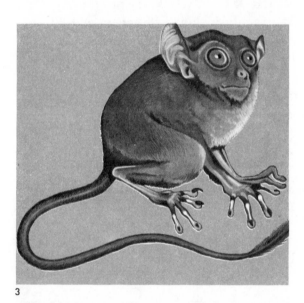

3

4

5

6

This means that the thumb can be placed opposite any of the fingers. As a result, primates can hold or pick up objects with their hands. Many primates have a similar arrangement of toes on the feet. The fingers and toes usually have nails instead of claws. Most primates live in social groups. They communicate with each other by sounds, touch, or smell. Primates have no definite mating season, and may mate at any time throughout the year.

The primates are divided into two main groups: the prosimians and the anthropoids. The prosimians include the aye-ayes, galagos, lemurs, lorises, pottos, tarsiers, and three species of shrew. (*See* LEMUR; SHREW; TARSIER.) The anthropoids include human beings, apes, and monkeys. (*See* APE; MONKEY.) In general, the anthropoids are larger and more intelligent than the prosimians. It is believed that the anthropoids evolved from the prosimians. (*See* EVOLUTION.) *See also* ANTHROPOID; HUMAN BEING; MAMMAL.

A.J.C./J.J.M.

PRIME MERIDIAN (prīm′ mə rid′ ē ən) The prime meridian is the imaginary north-south line that represents 0° longitude on maps of the world. It is also called the Greenwich meridian because it passes through Greenwich, England.

One hundred and eighty degrees of longitude are drawn both east and west of the prime meridian. The lines of 180° west longitude and 180° east longitude make up the same line. The prime meridian was established by a conference of astronomers in 1884. *See also* INTERNATIONAL DATE LINE; LATITUDE AND LONGITUDE. J.M.C./W.R.S.

PRIMROSE FAMILY The primrose (prim′ rōz′) family includes 28 genera and 800 to 1,000 species of perennial herbaceous plants. The are all dicotyledons. (*See* DICOTYLEDON.) Most grow in cooler areas of the northern hemisphere. The leaves are simple, with toothed margins. They usually grow in a

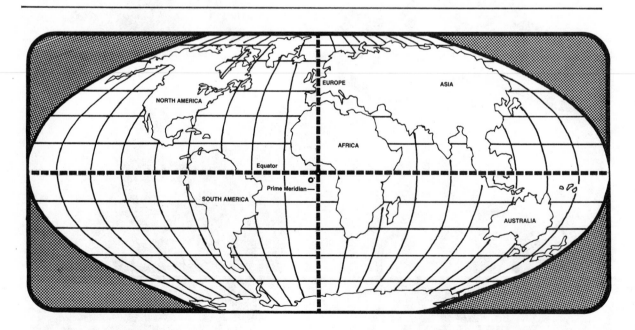

This map of the world shows the grid formed by parallels (running horizontally) and meridians (running vertically).

Shown above are several varieties of primrose.

rosette on the ground, but may be opposite or whorled on a stem. (*See* LEAF.) The flowers have five petals that are fused at the base to form a short tube. There are five stamens growing opposite the spreading petals. The fruits are capsules. (*See* FRUIT.)

Common primrose (*Primula vulgaris*) has given rise to many varieties of beautiful and colorful flowers. It has flowers which are yellowish-white in color. Each flower grows at the top of a leafless stalk. *See also* CYCLA-MEN. A.J.C./M.H.S.

PRINTED CIRCUIT (print′ ed sər′ kət) A printed circuit is an electrical device in which the wiring and certain components are made of a thin electrically conductive material applied in a pattern on an insulating substrate by a graphic art method.

In the past, electronic circuits were made of various parts connected together by wires.

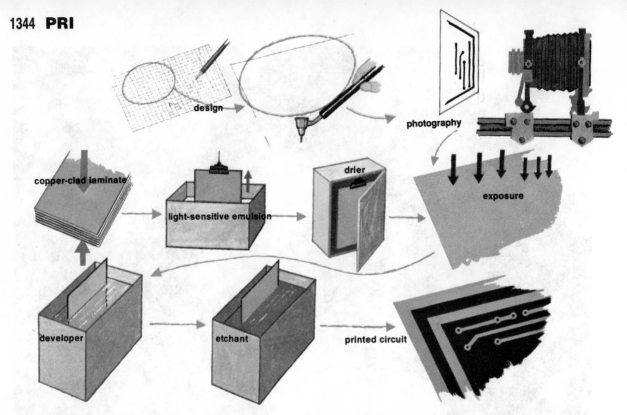

The parts, called components, included resistors, capacitors, and transistors. In most modern equipment, this method is no longer used. Instead, the components are mounted onto a flat sheet of plastic or similar material. Attached to the surface of this sheet is a network of copper strips. The copper strips are connected to the components by soldering. (*See* SOLDERING AND BRAZING.) This arrangement is known as a printed circuit.

The first step in making a printed circuit is to draw the network on paper. This is then photographed. The negative of the photograph has thin transparent lines in the shape of the network. The rest of it is black. The next step is to attach a thin layer of copper to a piece of plastic. The copper is coated with a substance that is sensitive to light. The negative is placed over the copper and the whole arrangement is exposed to light. The light affects only the exposed parts of the light-sensitive substance. The parts that are not affected are then removed by treatment with chemicals. This step is called developing. This leaves a layer of exposed copper under-

A printed circuit is made by photographing a design and transferring the negative to copper-coated plastic. This is placed in a light-sensitive emulsion and dried. The parts not affected by exposure are removed by chemicals in the developer, which leaves a layer of exposed copper underneath. In the etchant, the sheet is treated with more chemicals to remove the exposed copper. The layer of the light-sensitive substance which remains on the plate, can be removed to leave a network of copper strip—the printed circuit.

neath. The next stage is called etching. The sheet is treated with more chemicals to remove the exposed copper. This leaves a network of copper strips covered with a layer of the light-sensitive substance. The shape of the network is the same as the shape of the network in the photograph. The light-sensitive substance can then be removed to leave a network of copper strips.

Printed circuits are much cheaper to make than wired circuits. Another advantage of printed circuits is that they can be made more easily and with greater accuracy. Printed circuits are widely used in equipment such as televisions, radios, and computers.

M.E./L.L.R.

PRINTING

Printing (print' ing) is the process of placing inked impressions (marks made by pressure) of words, photographs, and artwork on paper or other material. Printing is one of our most important means of mass communication (communication that reaches great numbers of people). It forms the basis of our whole educational system and plays a vital role in the world of business and commerce.

Advertising, for example, depends largely on printing to sell goods and services.

The printing and publishing industry is the eighth largest industry in the United States. In addition to books, newspapers, and magazines, thousands of other items roll off printing presses each day. These items include calendars, ruled writing tablets, billboard signs, candy bar wrappers, food and beverage containers, wallpaper, textiles, post cards, mail order catalogs, comic books, and

This photograph shows the inside of a modern offset-printing plant.

reproductions of great works of art. Also, millions of tickets, pamphlets, and advertising circulars are printed.

Printing began in China around A.D. 500 with the use of simple wood printing blocks called woodcuts. For the next 900 years, everything people read was printed from such hand-carved wood blocks or copied by hand. In 1440, one of the greatest events in history took place—Johann Gutenberg of Germany invented printing with movable type. He made separate pieces of metal type for each letter to be printed. The letters could be used over and over again to print many different books.

Printing soon became the first means of mass communication. It put more knowledge into the hands of more people at a faster and cheaper rate than ever before. Gutenberg's invention was the start of modern printing.

Almost all printing is now done by one of three major processes: letterpress, offset lithography, or gravure. Each of these processes uses a different printing surface on the plate that does the printing. In letterpress, the printing surface is raised. In offset lithography, the printing surface is on a flat level. In gravure, the printing surface is below the regular surface of the plate.

Letterpress printing Letterpress is the oldest and most widely used printing process. It accounts for at least half the dollar value of all printing in the United States. Letterpress begins in the composing room of a printing plant. Raised metal letters are made by a Linotype machine and a Monotype machine. The Linotype casts full lines of metal type. All the letters and spaces are joined in a piece called a slug. The operator of the machine sits at a typewriterlike keyboard. When the operator strikes a key, a matrix, which is a mold for a particular letter, is released. After a line of matrices (plural of matrix) has been released, the machine pours molten (melted) metal into the molds. The metal hardens

quickly, and the finished slug drops into a tray called a galley. The Monotype casts separate letters instead of lines of type. It is made of two machines, a keyboard and a caster. The keyboard machine makes a paper tape with punched holes. The tape is fed into the casting machine. The holes in the tape form a code that is read by the caster to select the proper matrices. Molten metal is poured into the matrices and letters drop, one by one, to the galley, where they are assembled into words and lines.

Large type, such as the type used in newspaper headlines, is set by hand. The typesetter, or compositor, takes individual letters from a drawer called a case. He assembles the words, letter by letter, in a small tray called a composing stick. After the tray is full, he transfers the type to a galley.

The flat galley of letterpress type is assembled, or made up, into pages. Then a thick, wet cardboardlike material is pressed against the type. The raised type leaves impressions in the material. The cardboardlike material is placed in a curved mold because curved printing plates are needed for the press rollers, or cylinders. Molten metal is poured into the mold, and a curved printing plate is produced that fits on a cylinder in the press.

Illustrations in letterpress printing are produced by means of relief plates, called engravings. Engravings are made by a process known as photoengraving. There are two kinds of engravings: (1) line engravings, and (2) halftone engravings. Line engravings are made from artwork consisting of solid areas, or lines, such as drawings and diagrams. The photoengraver first takes a photo of the artwork. Then he or she places a negative on a metal plate coated with a light-sensitive substance. The photoengraver shines a bright light through the negative to transfer the image to the plate. The plate is developed with chemical and placed in an acid bath. The acid eats away the background, leaving the image in relief, or the raised image.

In this photo-engraving room, film is being prepared and inspected. Offset printing-plates will be made from the film.

Halftone engravings are made from photographs or other copy that has tones and shades. The photoengraver re-photographs the photograph through a clear plastic screen containing a regular pattern of thousands of tiny dots. The screen breaks up the image on the photo into tiny dots. The dots are large and closer together in the areas of the photo that are darkest and smaller and farther apart in lighter areas. The halftone negative is exposed to a metal plate coated with a light-sensitive substance. It is developed and placed in an acid bath. The acid eats away the non-printing areas and leaves the dots of the image area in relief. When the illustration is printed, the viewer's eyes blend the dots into duplicates of dark and light tones that were in the original image.

In letterpress printing, the impression is produced on the paper by inking the raised image on the plate and pressing the plate firmly against the paper in a press.

Offset lithography Lithography is a method of printing from a flat surface. It is based on the idea that grease and water do not mix. The process was discovered in 1796 by Aloys Senefelder, a German. Senefelder drew a design on a smooth, flat stone with a greasy crayon. He dampened the stone and water stuck only to the parts not covered by the design. Next, he inked the stone, and the greasy ink stuck only to the design. He then pressed paper against the stone, and transferred the image of the design to the paper.

Today, the same principle is used in offset lithography, often called offset printing. It is the fastest growing of all the printing processes. Photographic negatives are used to transfer images to thin metal plates. The plates can be easily bent to fit around printing cylinders in high-speed rotary presses. As the printing cylinders rotate, they press against water rollers, which wet the plates to create non-printing areas that will repel ink. The cylinders next pass against ink rollers. The greasy ink sticks only to the image areas of the plate. The printing cylinder finally passes, or offsets, the image onto a cylinder covered with a thick rubber mat, called a blanket. This rubber-coated cylinder, in turn, transfers the inked image onto the paper.

Type used in much offset printing is called cold type, or phototype. The process of producing the type is called photocomposition. Most of this type is produced on high-speed phototypesetting machines. A typical machine of this type is operated by a keyboard and makes paper galleys (wide strips) containing photographic images of letters, rather than actual metal type. Instead of a mold for each letter, such machines contain a reverse film image of each letter and symbol. When the operator strikes a key on the keyboard, a beam of light shines through the film and positions the image of the letter on photosensitive paper. After the words have been typed out by the operator, the machine automatically develops the images on the paper with chemicals. The paper strip containing the images of the type comes out of the machine ready for the next step, in which the typeset matter is pasted up into pages.

Electronic computers have simplified and speeded up the operation of most phototypesetting machines. The computers justify the type automatically. That is, they line up the left and right margins so that even columns of type are produced. They determine the proper spacing between letters and words so that each line is pleasing to the eye. The computers also hyphenate words at the ends of lines automatically. Computers are much faster than human operators at performing these tasks, but, unlike human beings are unable to make decisions, and an operator must often interfere to correct errors made by the machine. In large printing operations, such as newspapers, magazines, and books, typesetting operators work at terminals that may be some distance away from a central computer and a group of typesetting machines. The operators strike keys on a keyboard, and see the letters and lines reproduced on a television screen in front of them. After they have edited, or corrected, the text, they send a command to the computer. The command can tell the computer either to send the type on to the typesetting machines for setting or to store it for future use.

After being checked for accuracy and corrected, the paper strips of type are trimmed and waxed on the reverse side. They are then put in place on a piece of paper or cardboard. Wax is used to hold them in place. This phase is called paste-up.

The pasted up type is then photographed in a large camera, called a process camera. The negative is used to transfer the image to the thin metal plate that is used in the press.

Gravure printing Gravure printing is a method in which the images to be printed are sunk into the surfaces of the printing plates. It ranks third in use among the three major processes. Gravure printing is usually used to print fine color magazine sections, wedding invitations, and picture post cards. The copy to be reproduced is set in either hot metal, as for letterpress, or in cold type, as for offset printing, and then photographed. The negative is exposed to a thick copper plate coated with a light-sensitive substance. An acid bath then cuts the images into the surface of the plate.

The plate is curved to fit a printing cylinder in the press. As the cylinder rotates, it passes through a container of ink, called an ink trough. In this way, the sunken images receive the heavy supply of ink they need. After inking, a knifelike blade, called a doctor blade, automatically scrapes the ink from the upper surfaces of the plate. This leaves the ink only in the design that has been cut into the plate. An impression roller then presses the paper against the inked images, and the images are transferred to the paper.

Printing presses The simplest kind of printing press is the flatbed press. It can print from either raised or flat type. The bed is a flat table on which the type, or type plate, is

In the photograph above, printed packaging for toothpaste is being checked for color quality. In any color printing process, the quality and consistency of the color is carefully controlled. Modern presses which can print up to eight colors on the same press are called perfecting presses.

This large printing press (above) is used in lithography printing. Also called offset printing, lithography—often used for printing newspapers—is a method of printing from a flat surface.

placed. Rollers apply ink to the type, and a sheet of paper is pressed against it by another roller called a platen. Flatbed presses are slow in comparison to other presses. They are used to print such things as raffle tickets, leaflets, business cards, and advertising sheets.

Presses, like flatbed presses, that print on only one sheet of paper at a time are called sheet-fed presses. Presses that print from cylinders are called rotary presses. Rotary presses are faster than flatbed presses. The fastest rotary presses are web-fed presses, or web presses. The web is a long, continuous roll of paper that is fed through the press. Large web presses print on both sides of the paper at the same time and cut and fold it into complete publications, or sections called signatures. A large daily newspaper web press, for example, can produce as many as 60,000 complete papers in an hour.

Color printing In color printing, at least three separate printing plates must be made,

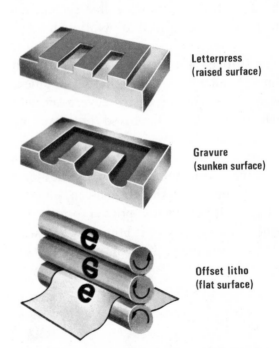

Letterpress
(raised surface)

Gravure
(sunken surface)

Offset litho
(flat surface)

There are three main kinds of printing: letterpress, gravure, and offset lithography. In letterpress printing, ink is transferred from a raised surface directly to the paper. In gravure printing, the ink is also transferred directly, but it is transferred from a sunken surface. In offset lithography, printing takes place from a flat surface, using three cylinders.

one each for red, yellow, and blue ink. A black plate, also, is usually made to add sharpness to the color. Separate negatives of these primary colors, called separations, are made and exposed to metal plates. Each separation has thousands of tiny dots in the color image. When the paper passes through the plates, which are mounted on separate cylinders, the different colored dots are printed one on top of the other. This action reproduces the shades and tones of color of the original illustration.

Some presses are capable of printing only one color at a time. Therefore, to print in full color, a sheet must be fed through the press as many times as there are colors. Modern presses can print up to eight colors on the same press, so that only one pass through the press is required for full color reproduction. Such presses are called perfecting presses.

Silk screen printing is a process for printing color designs on glass, textiles, wood, and plastics. Ink is squeezed through a stencil of the design, then through a fine screen, and finally onto the surface to be printed.

The future of printing Printing is continually undergoing change and development. Many of the old processes have been automated, and new, improved processes are being invented. Newspapers and books of the future may come rolling out of a special machine in your home; or, you may be able to watch printed material on a screen, and then select what you want in printed form. Whatever the form, however, printing will always play an important role in people's battle against ignorance.   W.R.P./R.W.L.

PRISM (priz′ əm) A prism is a transparent object that bends light and breaks it up into rainbow colors. Prisms can have many different shapes. The most common type has two end faces that are triangles. Joining these end faces are three oblong faces. In general, the end face can have any number of sides and the faces joining them can be parallelograms, not oblongs.

Prisms made from glass are used in optical instruments. Sometimes they are used for reflecting light. More often, they are used for dispersing light. If light hits the side of a glass prism at an angle, it bends as it passes into the prism. The amount that the light is bent depends on its color. For example, red light is bent less than blue light. White light is a mixture of colors. When white light enters a prism, it becomes separated into its various colors. This is called dispersion. (*See* DISPERSION OF LIGHT.)

Prisms are used for this purpose in instruments called spectroscopes. (*See* SPECTROSCOPE.) They are also used in other optical instruments such as microscopes. In microscopes, prisms are used for changing the direction of light and for splitting up the light. The splitting is done by shining a beam of light onto an edge of the prism. Part of the beam is reflected from one side and part from the other. Beam splitting is also used in binoculars.   M.E./J.D.

PROBABILITY (präb′ ə bil′ ət ē) Probability is a branch of mathematics that studies the laws of chance. A simple example of the laws of chance is tossing a coin. The coin can turn up either heads or tails. Both are equally likely. Therefore the probability of it being heads is ½ and the probability of it being tails is ½. If you toss two coins, the situation is a little more complicated. There are now four possibilities: head-head, head-tail, tail-head, and tail-tail. All four situations are equally likely. Therefore the probability of each is ¼. But head-tail is the same as tail-head. Therefore its probability doubles and is ½. The probabilities then are head-head (¼), tail-tail (¼), and head-tail (½). The total probability for all events always adds up to one.

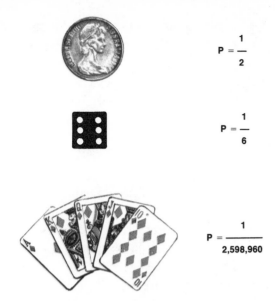

$$P = \frac{1}{2}$$

$$P = \frac{1}{6}$$

$$P = \frac{1}{2,598,960}$$

To calculate the probability (P) of an event happening, divide one by the number of ways in which the event can happen. A coin can fall in two ways, and a die is six ways. Some probabilities can be extremely small. The chance probability of choosing five particular cards from a deck of 52 cards is one in 2,598,960.

The probability of one coin turning up heads is ½ and the probability of tossing a coin twice and getting two heads is ¼. This shows that probabilities are combined by multiplying them together since ½ × ½ = ¼. In the same way, suppose that you toss a coin ten times. The probability of getting ten heads is ½ multiplied by itself ten times. This is 1/1024. There is one chance in 1,024 that you will land ten heads.

Probability never tells us what will happen in any particular case. It only predicts the likelihood. For example, it is equally likely that a coin will land heads or tails up. However, suppose that it lands heads up the first time. This does not mean that it will definitely land tails up the second time. The probability of this happening is still ½.

What is the probability of drawing a heart from an ordinary deck of cards? The number of possible outcomes is 52 (the number of cards in a deck), of which 13 are hearts. Therefore, the probability of getting a heart is 13/52 = ¼.

Probability is used in many fields where the chance of a certain event happening needs to be calculated. Insurance companies use probabilities to calculate the amount that they charge to their customers. Probability is also used in physics. For example, the behavior of a certain electron in an atom can never be accurately predicted. However, the likelihood of certain kinds of behavior can be calculated. M.E./S.P.A.

PROBOSCIS MONKEY (prə bäs′ əs mən′ kē) The proboscis monkey (*Nasalis larvatus*) lives in the trees in the swamps of Borneo. The male has a huge nose, or proboscis, that hangs down over his mouth. The female's nose is smaller, and the nose of a baby is small and upturned. A large male may grow 75 cm [30 in] long and have a tail at least that long. The male may weigh as much as 26 kg [55 lb]. The female is smaller and lighter. Both sexes have reddish-brown hair with light tan hair on the belly.

The male proboscis monkey has a huge nose, or proboscis, which hangs down over his mouth.

Proboscis monkeys are herbivores and usually eat leaves. They live in groups of about 20. After mating and a gestation period of about 166 days, the female gives birth to one offspring. (*See* GESTATION PERIOD.) *See also* MONKEY. A.J.C./J.J.M.

PROBOSCIS WORM (prə bäs′ əs wərm′) A proboscis worm is any of about 600 species of invertebrates belonging to the phylum Nemertea. They are the simplest animals with a complete digestive system and a closed circulatory system. In a complete digestive system, there is an opening where food enters (mouth) and a different opening through which wastes leave (anus). In a closed circulatory system, the blood always stays in vessels (arteries, capillaries, veins) and does not enter body spaces.

Proboscis worms are carnivorous and eat other small invertebrates. A proboscis worm captures prey by shooting out a muscular proboscis from a space just above the mouth. The proboscis is a spearlike structure that may be even longer than the worm itself. It is either sticky or armed with small, toothlike spears. The worm wraps its proboscis around the prey and pulls it back toward its mouth. The proboscis worm then either sucks the body fluids from the prey or eats it whole.

The bodies of proboscis worms are usually flattened and are not segmented, or divided up into rings. This gives rise to their common nickname, "ribbonworms." Most proboscis worms are about 20 cm [8 in] long, though they vary in length from 1 cm [0.4 in] to 2 m [6.5 ft]. Most live in shallow ocean water near the coasts in temperate (mild climate) areas. They are able to regenerate and sometimes reproduce asexually by fragmentation. (*See* REGENERATION.) In fragmentation, the worm breaks into many pieces. Each piece develops into a new worm. (*See* ASEXUAL REPRODUCTION.) Reproduction is usually sexual, however, and involves external fertilization. (*See* FERTILIZATION.)

Members of the genus *Glycera* of phylum Annelida are sometimes called proboscis worms. (*See* ANNELIDA.) They have a proboscis connected to the digestive tract. They are segmented worms that also live in temperate coastal waters. These annelids are sometimes called bloodworms. *See also* INVERTEBRATE; WORM. A.J.C./C.S.H.

PROCAINE (prō′ kān′) Procaine is a synthetic organic chemical that is widely used in dentistry and surgery as a local anesthetic. (*See* ANESTHETIC.) When injected, procaine deadens nearby nerves without harming them. Its effect wears off after a short time. Unlike some anesthetics, procaine is not poisonous or addictive.

Procaine was introduced in 1905 as a substitute for the then popular anesthetic, cocaine. Its chemical name is procaine hydrochloride, but it is commonly known by its trade name, Novocaine. In recent years, procaine has been replaced, in large part, by two new drugs, lidocaine and mepivacaine. These synthetic chemicals are faster, stronger, and longer lasting than procaine. *See also* DRUG. A.J.C./J.J.F.

PROCYON (prō′ sē än′) Procyon, or Little Dog Star, is a first magnitude star of the constellation Canis Minor. It is located about 11 light years from the earth.

Procyon is the brightest star of its constellation, as well as one of the most brilliant (sparkling) stars in the sky. It is a yellow-white color. A triangle is formed between Procyon, Betelgeuse (constellation Orion), and Sirius (constellation Canis Major). *See also* CANIS MAJOR AND MINOR; STAR. J.M.C./C.R.

PRODUCER GAS (prō dü′ sər gas) Producer gas is made by passing air over hot coal or coke. The air supply is controlled so that the coal or coke burns to form the gas carbon monoxide. If it were not controlled, carbon dioxide would be formed instead. Producer gas has about 30 percent carbon monoxide and 55 percent nitrogen from the air. It is used as a fuel for industry. When carbon monoxide is burned it produces carbon dioxide and heat. Producer gas is a poor quality fuel but can be made easily and cheaply. It is used mainly for heating furnaces. It is now being replaced by natural gas.   M.E./A.D.

PROJECT APOLLO (präj′ ekt′ ə päl′ ō) Apollo was the name for a large spaceflight project involving thousands of scientists, astronauts, technicians, and manufacturers assembled by NASA (National Aeronautics and Space Administration) in 1961. The aim of the Project was to land men on the moon and bring them back safely before 1970. It was set by President John F. Kennedy on May 25, 1961, and unanimously approved by Congress.

Project Apollo beat its deadline by half a year. Civilian Astronaut Neil Armstrong stepped from the lunar module "Eagle" onto the surface of the moon in July, 1969.

There were many problems at the beginning and in the early stages of Project Apollo. A rocket powerful enough to reach the moon had to be designed and built. New launching, training, and research bases were needed. A worldwide radio tracking network had to be set up.

The method chosen for the attempt at landing on the moon was called lunar orbit rendezvous. Three astronauts would travel to the moon in a three-part spacecraft. The crew would live in the command module. The service module would hold necessary equipment. The third part was the lunar module.

The whole spacecraft would orbit, or circle, the moon at great height. Two astronauts would climb into the lunar module (LM) and use it to go down to the surface of the Moon. Later, a part of the LM would bring the astronauts back to the command and service modules. The LM would be discarded before

The launch of a *Saturn V* moon rocket with an Apollo capsule at its tip is shown above. *Saturn V*, a powerful launch vehicle, was developed especially for Project Apollo.

Recovery of U.S. astronauts is made in the sea. After splashdown of the command module, astronauts leave the spacecraft and climb aboard a dinghy which takes them to the recovery ship.

Photographs from Apollo missions are shown above. Apollo 15 made the fourth moon landing (top photo) in the Apennine Mountains near Hadley Rille. Astronauts David Scott, James Irwin, and Alfred Worden spent three days on the moon in 1971. The electrically powered lunar rover (above left) was used for excursions on the surface of the moon. An astronaut (above right) is pictured preparing to drill a hole into the moon's topsoil. Astronauts gather samples of the moon's soil which are analyzed and provide valuable information.

the spacecraft returned to earth.

On January 27, 1967, Project Apollo had a serious setback. Astronauts Virgil Grissom, Edward White, and Roger Chaffee were burned to death in a fire aboard the spacecraft during a practice session. The spacecraft had to be redesigned. Flight testing resumed in October, 1968, with the earth-orbital mission, Apollo 7.

During December 1968, the first flight around the moon took place when Astronauts Frank Borman, James Lovell, and William Anders circled the moon ten times, transmitting a special television program on the occasion of Christmas.

This instrument module (far left) studied the moon's surface while in orbit around the moon.

Moon craters (left) were photographed from inside an Apollo capsule. Aristarchus (center), Herodotus (right), and Schroter's valley are shown.

On July 20, 1969, Armstrong and Edwin "Buzz" Aldrin landed on the moon in an area known as the Sea of Tranquillity. Michael Collins remained aboard the Apollo 11 command module in orbit. Armstrong and Aldrin stayed on the moon for 21 hours, 35 minutes.

In November, 1969, the Apollo 12 team landed Charles Conrad and Alan Bean on the moon, with Richard Gordon remaining on board the orbiting spacecraft.

In April, 1970, an explosion ripped open the service module of Apollo 13 when it was 320,000 km [200,000 mi] from earth. The crew and spacecraft were successfully brought back to earth, by swinging around the moon once.

Four successful Apollo moon landings followed. The last three lunar landing missions each carried a battery-powered four-wheeled car, the Lunar Rover, to let the astronauts do part of their exploring by driving rather than by walking. The final landing, Apollo 17, happened on December 11, 1972. Eugene Cernan and Harrison Schmitt spent 74 hours, 59 minutes on the moon and returned with 113.6 kg [250 lbs] of lunar material, while Ronald Evans stayed in the orbiting command module. *See also* SPACE TRAVEL.

W.R.P./J.VP.

PROJECTOR (prə jek′ tər) A projector is a device used to show enlarged pictures on a screen. Projectors are most commonly used to show photographic slides and movies.

The simplest projector consists of: (1) a light, (2) a reflector that focuses the light, (3) a focusing lens, and (4) a projector lens. A powerful light is needed to project images onto a screen. Most projectors use an incandescent bulb of about 1,000 watts. The reflector, located behind the bulb, is a concave (inward curving) mirror. It focuses the light rays forward through a thick focusing lens. The focusing lens is flat on the side facing the bulb, and convex (outward curving) on the other side. Light rays entering the lens are bent inward and brought together. The concentrated rays then pass through a photographic slide or film that is placed so that its image is upside down. The final lens, the projector lens, reverses and enlarges the picture, which appears right side up on the screen.

Some slide projectors can hold over 100 slides. A new slide is put in place to be projected, and the previous one is removed at the touch of a button.

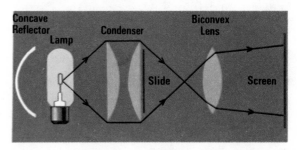

Features of a slide projector are shown above.

Slide projectors are used by teachers and business people to illustrate subjects being discussed. Lecturers also often use projectors in this way.

Movie projectors have electrically powered reels that move the film between the bulb and projecting lens at high speed. *See also* MOTION PICTURE; OPAQUE PROJECTOR.

W.R.P./S.S.B.

PROMETHIUM (prə mē′ thē əm) Promethium (Pm) is a radioactive metallic element. It is a member of the rare earth group of metals. (*See* RARE EARTH ELEMENT.) Its atomic number is 61. Promethium melts at about 1,100°C [2,000°F] and boils at about 2,500°C [4,500°F]. Its relative density is not yet known.

Promethium does not occur in nature. It was first isolated in pure form in 1945. It has 8 isotopes. (*See* ISOTOPE.) The longest-lived isotope is promethium-145. Half of it decays in 18 years. Promethium-145 gives off beta particles and is used as a source for those particles. It may also be used in the future as a portable source of X rays. *See also* BETA PARTICLE.

M.E./J.R.W.

PRONGHORN (prŏng′ hôrn′) The pronghorn (*Antilocapra americana*) is a hoofed mammal sometimes called the American antelope. (*See* UNGULATE.) However the pronghorn, which has branched horns, is not a true antelope. It has no close relatives, and is little changed from its ancestors, which lived more than a million years ago. Pronghorns live in North America, from Canada to central Mexico, and from Iowa to near the Pacific coast.

The pronghorn has a thick body, large ears, and thin legs. It varies in color from tan to reddish brown. The animal has white markings on its underparts, rump, head, and throat. The buck (male) stands about 89 to 104 cm [35–41 in] at the shoulder. It weighs about 45 to 64 kg [100– 140 lb]. The animal's

horns average 30 cm [1 ft] long, and have a black, horny covering. The pronghorn is the only animal in the world that regularly sheds the covering of its horns.

Pronghorns are grazers and live on open grassland. Each buck often lives with several mates. Does (females) usually bear twins in the month of May each year.

Pronghorns are social animals which gather into herds, especially in winter. They are probably the fastest large mammals of North America, known to run at a rate of 64 km [40 mi] per hour for about 3 km [2 mi]. Once an endangered species, pronghorns are now estimated to number at least 250,000. In several western states, hunting of the pronghorn is allowed.

J.J.A./J.J.M.

The pronghorn (above), is probably the fastest large mammal in North America. Pronghorns have been known to run at rates of 64 km [40 mi] per hour for about 3 km [2 mi].

PROPANE (prō′ pān′) Propane (C_3H_8) is a colorless inflammable gas. It is a hydrocarbon, since a propane molecule contains only the elements carbon and hydrogen. It is a member of the paraffin group of hydrocarbons. (*See* PARAFFIN.) Propane occurs in the natural gas found in deposits of petroleum. It is used as a fuel, often mixed with another paraffin, butane. It is also used for manufacturing other chemicals, ethene and propene, for example. These chemicals are used to make the plastics polyethylene and polypropylene.   M.E./J.M.

PROPELLER (prə pel′ ər) A propeller is a fanlike device mounted on a power-driven shaft that moves a ship or airplane forward by the action of its blades on water or air.

Marine propellers range in diameter from 25 cm [10 in] for small boats, to 244 cm [8 ft] for the average large ship. They are usually made of bronze and manganese.

The marine propeller bites into the water much the way a screw bites into wood. Water flows over the surface of the blades, and because of their specially designed airfoil shape, a force is produced that is parallel to the axis of the rotation of the propeller. The force drives the ship forward. The same principle applies to airplane propellers. (*See* AERO-DYNAMICS.)

The pitch of a propeller is the angle that the blades are set on the hub. Pitch also means the distance the propeller would advance (move forward) with each revolution if it were cutting into something solid, like wood. However, the marine propeller does not advance this full distance because water does not offer as much resistance as wood. The difference between the pitch and the actual distance the propeller does advance in water is called slip. Slip usually amounts to about 15 percent, even with the most efficient marine propeller.

Outboard motors and other marine engines used in small pleasure crafts usually have two-bladed propellers. Larger crafts have three or four-bladed propellers. Propellers on ships with a single engine rotate in a clockwise direction, when seen from the rear. Twin-engine vessels usually have propellers that rotate in opposite directions. The propeller on the right side rotates in a clockwise direction, and the propeller on the left side

rotates in a counterclockwise direction. Ships with one propeller that turns clockwise tend to veer to the right because of the direction of the propeller rotation. Helmsmen overcome this tendency with a slight correction in the steering. The opposite rotation of propellers on twin-engine ships does away with this problem. Twin-engine vessels (ships) are easier to handle than single-engine craft under power. Twin-engine vessels can make sharp turns by reversing the thrust of one propeller while the other one goes straight ahead.

Most airplanes today have variable-pitch propellers. The angle of the propeller blades can be adjusted while the propeller is spinning.

Airplane propellers have two or more blades fixed to a central hub. A fixed-pitch propeller is one in which the pitch, or angle of the blades, is fixed. Most airplanes today have variable-pitch propellers. The angle of the blades can be adjusted while the propeller is spinning. The adjustment is done either manually by the pilot or automatically to give the most efficient blade angle for different conditions of flight. Some propellers can be "feathered" in the event of engine failure— the blades can be rotated so that their leading and trailing edges are parallel to the path of flight. This lessens air resistance and prevents engine damage. Propeller-driven airliners and cargo planes have reversible-pitch propellers. The blades can be rotated so that the propeller produces reverse thrust. This helps heavy airplanes slow up and stop on short or icy runways where wheel brakes are not too effective. *See also* AIRPLANE; SHIPS AND SHIP-BUILDING.

W.R.P./R.W.L.

PROPRIOCEPTION (prō′ prē ō sep′ shən) Proprioception means "awareness of self." It is the internal sense through which the brain constantly receives information about the body's position, balance, and internal condition. Most animals have proprioceptors of some kind. Vertebrates have "position" receptors located in striated muscles and on the surfaces of tendons. (*See* MUSCLE; TENDON.) These receptors are necessary for coordinated movement of all muscles that are under conscious control. For example, proprioceptors keep the brain aware of the position of the arms. The brain can then send the proper signals to the muscles in the arm so that the arm moves in the desired way. Arthropods, such as insects, and some other invertebrates also have "position" receptors. They are located on the outside surfaces of the muscles and in the joints.

In order for an animal to keep its balance, it has proprioceptors that respond to gravity. Many invertebrates have a balancing structure called a statocyst. The statocyst is a fluid-filled chamber with tiny hairs and free-floating, sandlike granules. When the animal changes position, the granules float into the hairs, sending a signal to the brain. Most vertebrates have a similar structure in the ear. (*See* EAR.)

In human beings and many other animals, the proprioceptors signal a part of the brain called the cerebellum. (*See* BRAIN.) The cerebellum also processes the signals traveling from the brain to the muscles. The cerebellum brings together all these signals in order to regulate all of the voluntary (conscious) movements of the body. Because of this, the organism is able to keep its balance and move in a coordinated way. *See also* CYBENETICS; NERVOUS SYSTEM; VERTEBRATE.

A.J.C./J.J.F.

PROSPECTING

Prospecting (präs′ pekt′ ing) is looking for a place that shows signs of containing a mineral deposit. In the United States, early prospectors were enchanted by the promise of rich discoveries of gold, silver, and other precious metals. These people traveled over mountains throughout the West, often leading lonely lives and suffering terrible hardships. Most early prospectors had no scientific training. They depended mainly on luck to discover deposits. Their simple equipment included picks, shovels, and large, flat pans.

Modern prospecting Prospectors today are usually qualified geologists who have been trained in chemistry and physics. In their search for valuable metals, minerals, fuels, and water, they use a wide range of scientific equipment.

Prospectors now use geological maps. These maps show rock outcrops on the surface and also indicate how rock layers dip beneath the surface. Geologists can therefore use these maps to get information about underground structures. Aerial photographs, including infrared pictures from spacecraft, may show features that cannot easily be seen on the ground. Geologists can also analyze samples of rocks and determine their relative ages from fossils. In recent years, these scientists have been able to find out much about the rocks beneath the surface using geophysical and geochemical methods.

Smoke and dust (above) are spewed up from a refraction seismic shot in the Algerian Sahara desert. The truck in this photo contains instruments which are used for geophysical prospecting.

This hovercraft (below) is being used to lay a marine seismic line. Hovercrafts can be used in prospecting to survey shallow water, inshore areas of sandbars, mud flats, or coral reefs.

All these methods are used in the search for petroleum and natural gas. Geologists know that petroleum and natural gas are found mostly in sedimentary rocks, including sandstone and limestone. Large quantities of these fuels build up in special rock structures called structural traps. A very common type of trap is an upfold in rocks called an anticline. (*See* ANTICLINE; GEOLOGICAL MAP; PETROLEUM.)

Geophysical prospecting Geophysical prospecting includes seismology, the scientific study of earthquakes. Seismology is especially important in the search for oil and gas. Geophysicists set up explosives in the ground and so generate small tremors. Using an instrument called a seismograph, the geophysicists record the path of the seismic waves that travel through the earth's crust. Because rock strata of differing densities (thicknesses) reflect and refract seismic waves in different ways, seismic studies give much information about rock structures under the ground.

Another geophysical method involves the study of local variations in gravity. Using instruments called gravity meters, geophysicists can discover variations in rock densities and information about rock structures. Magnetometers are used to find minerals with magnetic properties. Magnetometer surveys are often carried out by aircraft. Measurements of electrical conductivity are especially useful to locate metallic ores, which are usually better conductors of electricity than nonmetallic minerals. The chief instruments used in prospecting for radioactive substances, such as uranium, are Geiger counters. Geiger counters measure the amounts of radioactive substances in rocks. (*See* GEIGER COUNTER.) Ultraviolet lamps cause certain minerals to give off definite colors.

Geochemical prospecting Geochemical prospecting applies the study of chemistry to

A gravity meter (above and left) measures variations of gravity in an area. The variations help prospectors locate buried mineral deposits.

the search for valuable minerals. For example, geochemists may find clues to important reserves of minerals from a chemical analysis of water, soil, or plants. The presence of trace elements at the ground surface may point out large deposits under the ground. (Trace elements are chemical elements in very small amounts.)

After collecting information by all available methods, prospectors drill holes in likely areas. They can then discover the richness and extent of deposits before extraction (removal) begins. Most searching is done for deeply buried deposits. Most surface deposits have been discovered. Such prospecting is undertaken only after careful study, because expensive equipment and workers are needed. *See also* GEOCHEMISTRY; GEOPHYSICS.

J.J.A./W.R.S.

PROSTAGLANDIN (präs′ tə glan′ dən) Prostaglandin is the name of a group of chemicals found in the bodies of mammals, including human beings. Prostaglandins play an important role in regulating the body's control systems, including the endocrine and central nervous systems. Many scientists consider the prostaglandins to be hormones or hormonelike substances. (*See* HORMONE.) Since prostaglandins were discovered in the early 1930s, at least 16 different kinds have been identified. All are types of fatty acids. (*See* FAT.)

Is is believed that prostaglandins help regulate blood pressure, pulse rate, smooth muscle contraction, stomach acid production, and the use of fat stored in adipose tissue (connective tissue in which fat is stored). Prostaglandins also help regulate production of hormones by various glands of the endocrine system, including the pituitary, thyroid, and adrenal cortex.

In the near future, prostaglandins may be used as drugs to treat many disorders such as asthma, arthritis, high blood pressure, and stomach ulcers. Because they stimulate contractions of the uterus in pregnant women, they may be used to induce labor in normal childbirth or for therapeutic abortions. (*See* REPRODUCTION.) *See also* MUSCLE; NERVOUS SYSTEM.

A.J.C./J.J.F.

PROSTHETICS (präs thet′ iks) Prosthetics is the branch of medicine and science that deals with the use of prostheses. A prosthesis is an artificial structure that is used as a replacement for a missing part of the body. Some prostheses such as artificial bones, joints, blood vessels, and heart valves are used internally, or inside the body. Most internal prostheses are made of stainless steel or some form of plastic.

Many prostheses are used to replace external body parts. As technology has progressed, these external prostheses have become more lifelike in appearance and use. Natural-looking prostheses are frequently used to replace missing eyes, arms, legs, hands, and feet. The most common use of prosthetics is in dentistry. Millions of people have one or more artificial teeth. Plastic surgeons depend heavily on prosthetics when repairing damaged or defective tissues. (*See* PLASTIC SURGERY.) *See also* MEDICAL ENGINEERING.

A.J.C./J.J.F.

PROTACTINIUM (prōt′ ak′ tin′ ē əm) Protactinium (Pa) is a radioactive metallic element. Its atomic number is 91 and its atomic weight is 231.04. The melting point of protactinium is not known definitely. It is less than 1,600°C [2,900°F]. Its relative density is 15.4.

Protactinium occurs in uranium ores such as pitchblende. It has 13 isotopes. (*See* ISOTOPE.) The first isotope, protactinium-234, was discovered in 1913 by the Polish chemist Kasimir Fajans. The longest-lived isotope is protactinium-231. Its half life is 34,000 years. It is the most common isotope in natural protactinium. *See also* RADIOACTIVITY.

M.E./J.R.W.

PROTECTIVE COLORATION (prə′tek tiv kəl ə rā′ shən) Protective coloration is color that makes an organism less visible to its enemies. Many animals have colors that make them difficult to see. They "blend in" with their surroundings. These animals are said to be camouflaged because they possess protective coloration. (*See* CAMOUFLAGE.)

There are many different types of protective coloration. In countershading, the lower part of the animal's body is light-colored and the upper part is dark-colored. In bright sunlight, this reduces the differences between the shadows and the animal's body. In object resemblance, an animal looks like something else, such as a rock, or sand. Disruptive coloration consists of bold color patterns that confuse enemies. (*See* WARNING COLORATION.) *See also* MIMICRY.   S.R.G./R.J.B.

PROTEIN (prō′ tēn′) A protein is a chemical compound that is made of a chain of amino acids. Proteins are necessary for the survival of every living organism. They work in many different ways. Enzymes, an important group of proteins, act as catalysts in many biochemical reactions. Enzymes are very important in the upkeep of an organism's metabolism. (*See* ENZYME; METABOLISM.) A disease-causing protein that is foreign to the victim is called an antigen. The effects of an antigen are offset by a protein called an antibody. (*See* ANTIBODY.) Some hormones, such as insulin, are also proteins. (*See* HORMONE.)

Proteins are made of amino acids. Each amino acid has carbon, nitrogen, oxygen, and hydrogen in it. Some also have small amounts of other elements. Plants make their own amino acids, and thus can make their own proteins. Animals (including human beings) are able to make some, but not all, of the necessary amino acids. Those that animals cannot make themselves are called the essential amino acids. Animals must get the essential amino acids from the food they eat. (*See* AMINO ACID.) When an animal eats protein-rich food, the proteins are broken down into individual amino acids. (*See* DIGESTION.) The amino acids are then used by the body to make proteins through a series of complicated chemical reactions known as protein synthesis in which the nucleic acids, DNA and RNA, play roles. (*See* NUCLEIC ACID.)

Protein-rich food is necessary for the well-being of an organism. Foods such as milk, eggs, fish, meats, and cheese have protein as well as the essential amino acids. Some foods do not have certain essential amino acids and are not considered good protein sources. (*See* NUTRITION.) Since humans cannot store amino acids, protein-rich food should be eaten every day to ensure the proper working of the body's metabolism. A great lack of protein may cause brain damage, mental retardation, and other unhealthy conditions. *See also* FOOD.   J.M.C./J.M.

PROTEROZOIC ERA (prät′ ə rə zō′ ik ir′ ə) The Proterozoic era is the final division of Precambrian time. Although the starting date of the Proterozoic era is in question, many geologists believe it began about 1.85 billion years ago. It ended about 570 million years ago, when the Cambrian period began.

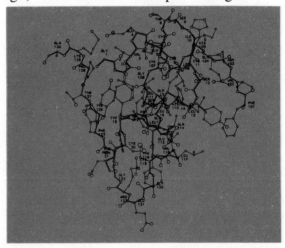

Some hormones, such as insulin, are also proteins. A model of the insulin molecule is shown above. A protein is a chemical compound made of a chain of amino acids. Proteins are necessary for life.

Proterozoic fossils include jellyfish, worms, and other primitive invertebrates. Much uplifting, folding, and volcanic activity of the earth's crust happened during the Proterozoic era. *See also* GEOLOGICAL TIME SCALE; PRECAMBRIAN TIME.   J.M.C./W.R.S.

PROTISTA (prə′ tis tə) Protista is a kingdom, in the five-kingdom system of classification, made up of one-celled animals. (*See* KINGDOM.) In this system, one-celled plants (bacteria and blue-green algae) belong to the kingdom Monera. In some other systems, however, kingdom Protista includes all one-celled organisms—both animals and plants. *See also* CLASSIFICATION OF LIVING ORGANISMS; PROTOZOA.   A.J.C./C.R.N.

PROTON (prō′ tän′) A proton is a very small particle in the nucleus of an atom and has a positive charge of electricity. All matter consists of very tiny particles called atoms. The atom is made up of a central core called the nucleus. Around the nucleus are particles called electrons. The nucleus contains two kinds of particles: protons and neutrons. (*See* NUCLEUS, ATOMIC.) Protons do not appear to be subject to the weak nuclear force of radioactive decay. (*See* PARTICLE PHYSICS.) However, physicists believe that protons may actually decay if given enough time, probably billions of years. They are now exploring this possibility using particle accelerators. (*See* ACCELERATORS, PARTICLE.)

The proton is a subatomic, or elementary, particle. Most elementary particles are unstable. That is, they break down into other particles. The proton is one of the few stable elementary particles. It has a positive charge. The size of its charge is equal to the size of the charge on the electron. However, the electron has a negative charge. If an atom has no charge, then the numbers of protons and electrons are equal. The proton also has spin. It spins around its own axis like a spinning ball.

The proton was discovered by the British physicist Lord Rutherford in 1919. (*See* RUTHERFORD, LORD ERNEST.) Physicists produce beams of protons in large machines called particle accelerators. These beams are used for making particles collide into each other. In this way, physicists can learn about the nature of the proton. Physicists used to think that the proton had no structure but they now believe that it does. Physicists think that the proton is made up of three particles called quarks. These quarks are very tightly bound together to form a proton. (*See* QUARK.)

The sun sends large numbers of protons out into space. Some of these protons reach the earth. Because they have an electric charge, they become trapped in the earth's magnetic field. These trapped protons form a belt of radiation around the earth. Other particles from the sun also form belts around the earth. These belts are called Van Allen belts. *See* VAN ALLEN BELTS.   M.E./J.T.

PROTOPLASM (prōt′ ə plaz′ əm) Protoplasm is the jellylike living material that makes up the cells of all living organisms. (*See* CELL.) It is mostly water, and contains many dissolved chemicals and chemical compounds. Protoplasm responds to touch and to changes in temperature. It "eats" food and takes away wastes. It "breathes" and reproduces. In most cells, the nucleus and cytoplasm is made of protoplasm. It is surrounded by a cell membrane. *See also* LIFE.
          A.J.C./C.R.N.

PROTOZOA

Protozoa (prōt′ ə zō′ ə) is a phylum of one-celled organisms, most of which are microscopic. The phylum Protozoa belongs to kingdom Protista. (*See* PROTISTA.) The name protozoa means "first animal." Since protozoans have many characteristics of animals, they are often considered to be animals. At one time, they were classified as part of the animal kingdom. (*See* CLASSIFICATION OF LIVING ORGANISMS.) There are about 30,000 identified species of protozoans. There are many more unidentified species, and many other species which are now extinct. Protozoans range in size from the smallest, a parasite in red blood cells that measures 0.0002 cm [0.00008 in] in diameter to the largest, a radiolarian measuring 5 cm [2 in] in diameter. Protozoans live in many environments. Most live in salt or fresh water. Some live in the soil, while others are parasites or live in the bodies of other organisms. (*See* PARASITE.) Protozoa make up most of the zooplankton found in the oceans. (*See* PLANKTON.)

Kinds of protozoans   Since the body of a protozoan is made up of only one cell, that cell must carry on all the functions of life. (*See* CELL.) It eats, breathes, takes away wastes, reproduces, and responds to the environment. Some protozoans have the simplest possible cellular structure. Others are the most complex cells known. The protozoans are usually divided into four groups, according to the way that they move from one place to another.

The flagellates are the most primitive of the protozoans. They have one or more long, whiplike flagella with which they swim about. (*See* FLAGELLUM.) They are usually oval in shape. Some, such as euglena and volvox, contain chlorophyll. (*See* VOLVOX.) They are able to make at least part of their own food. (*See* PHOTOSYNTHESIS.) Because they have chlorophyll, these protozoans are sometimes classified in kingdom Monera. (*See* MONERA.) Most flagellates live in the bodies of other organisms, often as parasites. One of these, Trypanosoma, causes African sleeping sickness. (*See* TRYPANOSOME.)

The sarcodina are protozoans that move by ameboid movement. In ameboid movement, the organism sends out pseudopodia or

"false feet." These pseudopodia are masses of protoplasm that let the organism "ooze" from one place to another. The most familiar sarcodinian is the ameba. (*See* AMEBA.) Many sarcodinians live in the bodies of human beings and other animals. Some are parasites while others live symbiotically. (*See* SYMBIOSIS.) Two of the most important sarcodinians are the radiolarians and the foraminiferans. The radiolarians have silica skeletons which pile up on the ocean floor when the organisms die. (*See* RADIOLARIAN.) These skeletons are the source of ooze. (*See* OOZE.) The foraminiferans have limestone shells which also pile up on the ocean floor. (*See* FORAMINIFERA.) These shells are the source of chalk. (*See* CHALK.)

The sporozoa are tiny protozoans that usually reproduce by spores. They are all parasites. The best known of the sporozoans is *Plasmodium*, a malaria-causing protozoan. (*See* PLASMODIUM.)

The ciliates are the most complex of the protozoans. They have tiny, hairlike cilia which help them move about in search of food. (*See* CILIUM.) The ciliates have two nuclei. The large macronucleus controls cellular activity and asexual reproduction. The smaller micronucleus works in sexual reproduction. Sexual reproduction is unusual among the protozoans, and happens only among ciliates. Some ciliates have special structures for getting food. For example, the

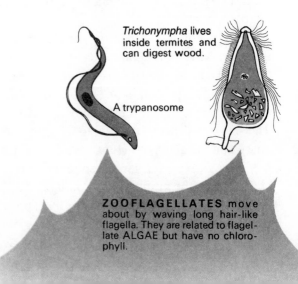

Trichonympha lives inside termites and can digest wood.

A trypanosome

ZOOFLAGELLATES move about by waving long hair-like flagella. They are related to flagellate ALGAE but have no chlorophyll.

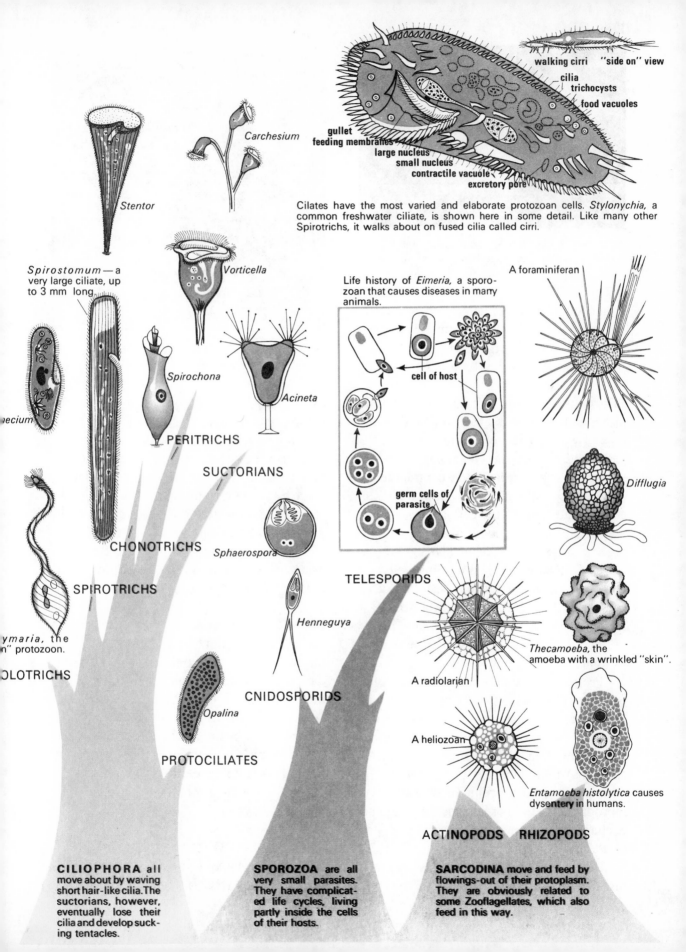

walking cirri   "side on" view
cilia
trichocysts
food vacuoles
gullet
feeding membranes
large nucleus
small nucleus
contractile vacuole
excretory pore

Cilates have the most varied and elaborate protozoan cells. *Stylonychia*, a common freshwater ciliate, is shown here in some detail. Like many other Spirotrichs, it walks about on fused cilia called cirri.

Stentor

Carchesium

Spirostomum — a very large ciliate, up to 3 mm long.

Vorticella

Spirochona

Acineta

PERITRICHS

SUCTORIANS

...ecium

A foraminiferan

Life history of *Eimeria*, a sporozoan that causes diseases in many animals.

cell of host

germ cells of parasite

Difflugia

CHONOTRICHS

Sphaerospora

TELESPORIDS

SPIROTRICHS

...ymaria, the
"...n" protozoon.

Henneguya

A radiolarian

Thecamoeba, the amoeba with a wrinkled "skin".

...OLOTRICHS

CNIDOSPORIDS

Opalina

A heliozoan

Entamoeba histolytica causes dysentery in humans.

PROTOCILIATES

ACTINOPODS   RHIZOPODS

CILIOPHORA all move about by waving short hair-like cilia. The suctorians, however, eventually lose their cilia and develop sucking tentacles.

SPOROZOA are all very small parasites. They have complicated life cycles, living partly inside the cells of their hosts.

SARCODINA move and feed by flowings-out of their protoplasm. They are obviously related to some Zooflagellates, which also feed in this way.

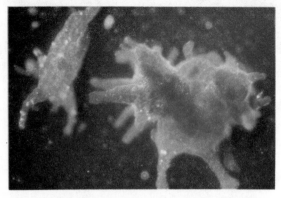

An ameba, a kind of protozoan which moves by flowing, can be recognized by the way it flows.

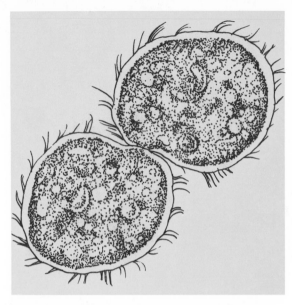

Protozoans usually reproduce asexually by fission. A ciliate (above) has split into new organisms.

paramecium has a ciliated oral groove that directs food into the mouth. (*See* PARA-MECIUM.) Another, the vorticella, creates a tiny whirlpool to bring food into its mouth.

Life of protozoans Protozoans are found throughout the world. Most are found in some type of water. The free-living protozoans digest food in enzyme-containing food vacuoles. Many protozoans have contractile vacuoles, special structures that squirt wastes and excess water out of the cell.

Most protozoans move away from foreign objects, bright light, chemicals, and very hot or very cold areas. This is a primitive type of response and is called avoidance. It is different from the nervous system response of higher animals. Some protozoans have a bright red "eye-spot" which may be sensitive to light.

Protozoans usually reproduce asexually by fission. (*See* ASEXUAL REPRODUCTION.) In fission, an organism splits into two new organisms. Some protozoans reproduce asexually by budding. (*See* BUDDING.) Some (the sporozoa) reproduce by spores. Others (the ciliates) undergo a primitive type of sexual reproduction. Two organisms join together, exchange nuclear material, separate, and then divide by fission.

If environmental conditions begin to threaten protozoans, some are able to survive by forming cysts. A cyst is an inactive or resting stage which is very tough. It can live in very hot or very cold temperatures. It can live without water or oxygen for long periods of time. These cysts are carried from place to place by the wind or by animals. Once the cyst is exposed to water, it develops into a new protozoan. Some disease-causing protozoans are especially dangerous because they form cysts which help an infection to spread quickly. (*See* DYSENTERY.)   A.J.C./E.R.L.

PROXIMA CENTAURI (präk′ sə mə sen′ tȯr′ i) Proxima Centauri is the closest star to the sun. It is the faint red dwarf that is part of the Alpha Centauri triple star system. Proxima Centauri belongs to the constellation Centaurus. It is visible from the northern hemisphere south of the 28th parallel.

Proxima Centauri is located about 4.3 light years from the earth. It has a magnitude of 11.3. *See also* ALPHA CENTAURI; CENTAURUS; STAR.   J.M.C./C.R.

PRUSSIC ACID (prəs ik′ as′ əd) Prussic acid is the name sometimes used for hydrocyanic acid (HCN). Hydrocyanic acid is a solution of the colorless gas hydrogen cyanide in water. It is a colorless liquid with a smell like that of bitter almonds. It is extremely poisonous and is used for fumigating (removing germs that might cause disease). The hydrogen cyanide is made on the spot by reacting potassium or sodium cyanide with sulfuric acid. Hydrogen cyanide is very important in industry, where it is used to make plastics and synthetic fibers and rubbers.

As with all acids, the hydrogen atom in a molecule of hydrogen cyanide can be replaced by a metal atom. This gives salts of hydrogen cyanide called cyanides. The hydrogen atom can also be replaced by an organic group of atoms. An example is the methyl group – CH_3. The group can join either onto the carbon atom or onto the nitrogen atom. If the group joins onto the carbon atom, compounds called cyanides or nitriles are formed. An example is methyl cyanide (CH_3– CN). If the group joins onto the nitrogen atom, the compounds are called isocyanides, or isonitriles. An example is methyl isonitrile (CH_3–NC).   M.E./J.M.

PSILOPHYTE (sī′ lə fīt′) The psilophytes are the most primitive of the vascular plants. (*See* VASCULAR PLANT.) The vascular plants have special structures for moving food and water from one part of the plant to another. During the Paleozoic era, about 400 million years ago, the psilophytes grew as large as trees. They were in great forests throughout the world. Today, all but two genera of psilophytes are extinct. These surviving plants are mostly tropical.

The psilophytes do not have true roots. Instead, they have special, rootlike underground stems called rhizomes. (*See* RHIZOME.) The aboveground stems are green and have many tiny openings called stomata. (*See* STOMA.) Most of the photosynthesis in these plants takes place in the stems. The leaves may be missing, scaly, or spinelike. They contain very little chlorophyll.

Psilophytes undergo alternation of generations. (*See* ALTERNATION OF GENERATIONS.) The sporophyte, or asexual stage is prominent. Its spores grow into tiny, saprophytic plants called prothallia. (*See* SAPROPHYTE.) The prothallia are the gametophytes. Frequently, the prothallia live symbiotically with a type of fungus. (*See* SYMBIOSIS.) The prothallia produce male gametes, or sperm, in antheridia, and female gametes, or eggs, in archegonia. After fertilization the zygotes grow into sporophytes. *See also* FOSSIL; PALEOBOTANY; PLANT KINGDOM.

A.J.C./M.H.S.

Psilophytes are known from fossils of the Silurian period. The drawing, far left, is a reconstruction of *Zosterophyllum*, which appears to have been a very simple plant. Sporangia can be seen at the tips of the branches. The drawing, left, is of *Psilotum*, a modern psilophyte—sometimes classified as a Psilote.

PSYCHIATRY (sə kī′ ə trē) Psychiatry is the branch of medicine concerned with the treatment and prevention of mental illness. A psychiatrist is a person who, after being trained as a physician, or medical doctor, takes three or more years of training in the treatment of mental illness. (*See* DOCTOR.)

Many techniques are used in treating the mentally ill. Psychiatrists use five basic methods of treatment. One method is called psychotherapy. Psychotherapy is mainly concerned with discussions between the patient and the psychiatrist. The patient discusses his problems with the psychiatrist. In turn, the psychiatrist tries to build the patient's confidence and help the patient develop a better outlook on life. Some psychiatrists use hypnotism to help them understand the patient's problems. (*See* HYPNOSIS.) Sometimes groups of patients take part in "group therapy." Such patients, meeting as a group with the psychiatrist, help each other understand themselves. The psychiatrist may try to get his patients to act out their problems in little plays called "psychodramas." When working with a child, a psychiatrist often uses "play therapy." In play therapy, instead of the child trying to talk about a problem, he acts it out with games or toys.

Psychoanalysis, a form of psychotherapy, is another method that psychiatrists use to treat the mentally ill. Psychoanalysis is based on the theory that the causes of many mental illnesses are buried in the unconscious. A patient may have no idea of what is causing his problems. The psychiatrist, by uncovering the causes, helps the patient understand his problems. (*See* PSYCHOANALYSIS.)

Behavioral therapy is another basic method used by psychiatrists. In this kind of therapy, rewards and punishments are used to help patients to act in a healthy way.

Drug therapy sometimes gives help for certain kinds of mental illnesses, especially types of neuroses and psychoses. Tranquilizers are drugs which help to calm a patient. Sedatives dull the senses of excited patients. (*See* SEDATIVE; TRANQUILIZER.)

If a patient does not respond to drugs, some psychiatrists apply electric shocks. In shock therapy, the psychiatrist passes a mild electric current through the patient's brain.

Whatever treatment, or combination of treatments, psychiatrists use depends on various factors, such as the type, cause, and extent of the mental illness. *See also* ADLER, ALFRED; FREUD, SIGMUND; JUNG, CARL GUSTAV; MENTAL HEALTH; PSYCHOLOGY; PSYCHOSOMATIC DISORDER.   J.J.A./J.J.F.

PSYCHOANALYSIS (sī′ kō ə nal′ ə səs) Psychoanalysis is a method of treating mental illness. The method was developed in the late 1800s and early 1900s by Sigmund Freud, an Austrian psychiatrist and psychologist. Other psychiatrists developed variations of Freud's technique. A psychoanalyst is a person, often a psychiatrist, who has had several years of training in psychoanalytic principles.

Psychoanalysis is based on the theory that unpleasant experiences, especially during childhood, may become buried in a person's unconscious (nonthinking) mind and cause mental illness. That is, a person's conscious thoughts and actions are influenced by unconscious mental processes. (*See* CONSCIOUSNESS.) Psychoanalytic treatment tries to bring these experiences out of the patient's unconscious and into his or her conscious mind. By doing this, the patient may be able to see and understand the cause of his problems. This understanding often helps the patient to adjust to life with less fear or anger.

Psychoanalytic treatment usually includes a method of "free association" to search a patient's unconscious and discover the cause of illness. In this method, the patient relaxes on a bed or couch. The psychoanalyst tries to get the patient to talk about anything that comes to his or her mind. Sometimes the patient's dreams are discussed. Dreams may give clues to the patient's unconscious.

The patient may find it difficult or refuse to talk freely at first. But when the patient begins to trust the psychoanalyst, the analyst can help the patient understand his inner problems.

Sessions of psychoanalysis may take place several times each week for months, or possibly years. In a few cases, a psychoanalyst may employ hypnosis. (*See* HYPNOSIS.)

Psychoanalysis is thus a method of psychotherapy. It is used most often for patients suffering from neuroses, which are mild mental disorders. *See also* FREUD, SIGMUND; MENTAL HEALTH; PSYCHIATRY; PSYCHOLOGY.   J.J.A./J.J.F.

PSYCHOLOGY

Psychology (sī kāl′ ə je) is the branch of science concerned with why human beings and animals behave as they do. The word psychology comes from the Greek words *psyche,* meaning "mind," and *logos,* meaning "study of." Psychology is therefore a very broad science. Studies in psychology range from the ability of mice to learn the path through a maze to the causes of international tensions.

Psychologists are interested in all human and animal experience—how creatures learn to perform various tasks, how they solve problems, how the senses work, and what the reasons are for people's motives, thoughts, feelings, and emotions. Though psychologists have learned much about behavior and experience, there is a great deal about which little is known. There is also a lot to be discovered.

Psychology is frequently grouped with biology, sociology, and anthropology as one of the behavioral sciences. Psychology is also related to psychiatry. Psychology is the study of human behavior, normal and abnormal. Instead of first being trained as physicians, or medical doctor, most psychologists have an M.A. or Ph.D. degree in psychology. (*See* DOCTOR.)

History   Psychology was once just a field of study within philosophy. In ancient times, Plato, Aristotle, and other philosophers developed theories about the causes of behavior and the relationships between mind and body. For many years, however, psychology was not established as a science based on careful observation and experiment.

Psychology became established as a science in 1879, when Wilhelm Wundt set up the first psychological laboratory in Leipzig, Germany. From the late 1800s until the 1930s, four different ways of studying the mind were developed. These methods or "schools" are structuralism, behaviorism, gestalt psychology, and psychoanalysis.

Structural psychologists, such as Wundt, believed the main purpose of psychology was to describe and analyze the way people experience or perceive things through their senses. For instance, the sense of sight gives the mind a great deal of information, such as color, size, shape, and distance. The sense of touch gives information about texture, heat, cold, pain, softness, hardness, wetness, and so on. Structural psychologists wanted to find out what kind of information the mind was getting. Introspection was the chief method that these psychologists used. Introspection takes place when a person observes his own experiences when stimulated, or made active, by some object or event.

In 1913, John B. Watson, an American psychologist, introduced behaviorism into psychology. Behaviorism was a reaction against the structural method of introspection. Watson called for the study of the behavior of people and animals, not of their experiences. The behavioral psychologists began laboratory experiments on the way people and animals behave in various situations. Ivan Pavlov had conducted experiments on the reflexes of dogs. (*See* PAVLOV, IVAN.) Behavioral psychologists continued these experiments to find out how people or animals usually behave—if behavior can be changed, and how it can be changed. Most psychologists agree that their science should study behavior, using mainly experimental methods. But some psychologists also believe that the behavioral psychologists ignored many important factors, including such problems as thought processes and personality development.

In about 1912, Max Wertheimer began developing gestaltism in Germany. In the 1930s, Wertheimer and his associates moved to the United States, where they headed the gestalt movement. Gestalt is a German word meaning ''pattern,'' or ''form.'' Gestalt psychologists believed that people perceive things in patterns or groups, not individual parts that are added together. For example, if a person looks at an automobile, he sees all at once a whole object that has windows, doors, tires, and so on. He does not first see each tire, each door, and each window separately. Gestalt psychologists created tests to determine the patterns of perception (the ability to be aware of things and understand them through the senses, especially sight) that people have. The most famous of these is the inkblot test. In such a test, a person describes what he sees in the inkblot. Gestalt psychologists attacked the views of structural psychologists that experience could be broken down into its parts, such as seeing, hearing, and touching. Gestalt psychologists believed that all these factors must be studied together in order to understand their relationships.

Psychoanalysis began in the early 1900s with the work of Sigmund Freud. According to Freud, a person tends to repress (push out of his conscious, thinking mind) any thoughts or memories that he or other people do not approve of. These repressed thoughts have a great effect on a person's behavior. (*See* FREUD, SIGMUND; PSYCHOANALYSIS.) Though many psychologists today do not agree with many of Freud's statements, Freud is given credit for showing how unconscious events can influence behavior.

Psychologists use a variety of methods to gather information about behavior. The main techniques include experiments, case histories, and surveys.

Branches of psychology Psychology is divided into several major specialties. Experimental psychology is concerned with laboratory research on humans and animals to find out what causes behavior. Physiological psychology is concerned with the relationship between behavior and the function of the nervous system, including the various organs of the body. The psychology of learning deals with how people learn, that is, how people get ideas and put them to use. One branch of the psychology of learning, called educational psychology, studies the problems of learning in schools. Another branch, called cognitive psychology, studies how the mind uses memory to store and retrieve information. Child psychology is the study of the growth and development of babies and children. (*See* PIAGET, JEAN.)

The psychology of individual differences is concerned with discovering why people act in the same way as or differently from each other. Psychologists in this field have developed many different kinds of tests to find out about people's individual characteristics. Some tests measure a person's interests—his likes and dislikes. Other tests measure how well a person does certain tasks in comparison with other people of the same age and similar background. Some tests measure aptitudes (the things a person has a talent for), personality, achievement (what a person has learned so far), and attitude (opinions).

Abnormal psychology is the study of mental or emotional problems. Psychologists, often working with psychiatrists, try to find out the causes of these problems and suggest ways of working them out. Social psychologists study the behavior of people in groups. For example, a social psychologist may study how a group of sixth graders behaves toward a group of third graders. Personnel or industrial psychologists try to discover what kind of job a person is suited for. They try to help workers who have problems in getting along with other workers.

A recent branch of psychology is parapsychology, which is the study of powers of extrasensory perception.

Psychology in daily living To understand why we behave as we do and how we experience things as we do is of great importance in our daily lives. Such an understanding helps people get used to situations. Also, by learning to understand themselves, people can lessen their worries and fears.

People also want to discover their skills and aptitudes. Such factors can help them in selecting a career which could make them happy and successful. Understanding human behavior helps people teach children, both at home and in school. It can also guide them in getting along better with each other and making peace among various groups of people or nations. Psychologists study these problems through trained observation and careful experimentation. *See also* DREAM; EMOTION; EXTRASENSORY PERCEPTION; HALLUCINATION; HYPNOSIS; INSTINCT; INTELLIGENCE; LEARNING AND MEMORY; MENTAL HEALTH; PERCEPTION; PSYCHIATRY; PSYCHOANALYSIS.

J.J.A./J.J.F.

PSYCHOSOMATIC DISORDER (sī′ kə sə mat′ ik dis ȯrd′ ər) A psychosomatic disorder is a physical illness that is caused or chiefly influenced by the emotional state of the patient. The term psychosomatic comes from the Greek words *psyche,* meaning ''mind,'' and *soma,* meaning ''of the body.'' Physicians know that emotional disturbances often affect a person's body. For example, when a person is angry or afraid, adrenalin flows into the blood and speeds up the action of the heart. (*See* EMOTION.)

There are various physical illnesses that seem to be related to emotional disturbances. Among these are asthma, stomach ulcers, rheumatoid arthritis (stiffness of the bone joints), and hypertension (high blood pressure). The disorder known as hysteria, in which mental problems can cause such physical symptoms as seeming paralysis of an arm, is not considered a psychosomatic disorder. This is because the ''paralyzed'' arm has nothing physically wrong with it. The nerves and muscles are capable of working normally, but a mental problem prevents this.

Physicians have found that psychosomatic disorders require both medical treatment and psychiatric treatment if the patient is to be made well again.   J.J.A./J.J.F.

PTERIDOPHYTE (tə rid′ ə fīt′) The pteridophytes are a large group of simple vascular plants. (*See* VASCULAR PLANT.) They include the ferns, horsetails, and club mosses. Although these plants do not have flowers, they do have true roots, stems, and leaves. The pteridophytes grew in great forests about 250 million years ago, near the end of the Paleozoic era. (*See* PLANT KINGDOM.) With the exception of some tropical tree ferns, the living pteridophytes are small, herbaceous plants. The pteridophytes, like many other lower plants, undergo alternation

Horsetails are pteridophytes which reproduce by spores which develop on small cones at the top of their fertile stems. Pteridophytes grew in great forests about 250 million years ago.

The pterodactyl (above) was a prehistoric winged reptile, which had batlike wings. Pterodactyls probably lived on cliffs by the sea, and glided down to catch food. Their wings were useful for gliding, but pterodactyls could not actually fly. These reptiles lived from about 150 million to 65 million years ago, during the Jurassic and Cretaceous periods.

of generations. (*See* ALTERNATION OF GENERATIONS.) *See also* CLUB MOSS; FERN; HORSETAIL.   A.J.C./M.H.S.

PTERODACTYL (ter′ ə dak′ tl) The pterodactyl was a prehistoric winged reptile. It lived from about 150 million to 65 million years ago, during the Jurassic and Cretaceous periods. Modern birds are not descended from the pterodactyls.

There was a great range in the sizes of pterodactyls. Some were about the size of a small bird, while others were about 4.8 m [15 ft] long. The smaller pterodactyls were the first to evolve.

The pterodactyls had batlike wings. Their front legs had four fingers. The first three fingers were free, but the last one was much longer, extending along half the length of the wing. Membranes connected the bony fourth finger with the pterodactyl's body and hind legs. The wing span ranged from 0.3 to 15.5 m [1 to 50 ft]. Although the wings were useful for gliding, the pterodactyl could not actually fly. Apparently, pterodactyls lived on cliffs from which they glided down to get food.

The pterodactyl's big head had a toothed, birdlike beak. Its body was covered with leathery, hairless skin. Its tail was either very small or not there at all. Pterodactyls did not show nesting habits. The reason for their extinction at the end of the Cretaceous period is uncertain. *See also* CRETACEOUS PERIOD; JURASSIC PERIOD; REPTILE.   J.M.C./R.J.B.

PTOLEMY (täl′ ə mē) Ptolemy was a Greek scientist who lived in the second century A.D. Very little is known about his life. Even the years of his birth and death are not known. Ptolemy studied astronomy, mathematics, and geography. He wrote a series of books called the *Almagest*. These books contained all that was known about astronomy at that time. In them, Ptolemy presented his system of the universe. He thought that the earth was at the center of the universe and all the objects in the universe revolved around the earth. He also wrote a book on geography. In this book, the idea of latitude and longitude was introduced for the first time. *See* LATITUDE AND LONGITUDE.   M.E./D.G.F.

PUFF ADDER (pəf′ ad′ ər) The puff adder is a poisonous snake that belongs to the viper family Viperidae. It is a thick, large-headed snake that can reach 1.8 m [6 ft] long. The puff adder eats lizards and small mammals. There are many species of puff adders. They live in the forests, deserts, and grasslands of Africa. *See also* ADDER; SNAKE.

S.R.G./R.L.L.

A coiled puff adder is shown above.

PUFFIN (pəf′ ən) A puffin is a seabird that belongs to the auk family Alcidae. (*See* AUK.) It is a stocky bird with a short tail and wings. The puffin grows to 27.5 to 30 cm [11 to 12.5 in] in length. It has an unusually tall, orange and yellow bill, white face, and a dark brown back and wings. Three species of puffin live off the coasts of North America. The horned puffin and the tufted puffin live in the North Pacific Ocean while the common puffin is found in the North Atlantic Ocean. All three species spend most of the time on the open ocean where they feed on fish and shellfish. They come ashore only to breed. When they are breeding, the puffins are found in large numbers on rocky islands and coastlines.

S.R.G./L.L.S.

The puffin (above) is a seabird with a brightly colored bill. It comes ashore only to breed.

PULSAR (pəl′ sär′) A pulsar is a rapidly spinning star that gives off rhythmic pulses of radiation. The term pulsar stands for "pulsating radio star." British astronomers discovered the first pulsar in 1967. Today, more than 100 pulsars are known to exist.

Pulsars give off radiation at a rate of 1 pulse per .03 second to 1 pulse per 4 seconds. The pulses are given off over a wide range of radio frequencies. High energy particles let loose from the pulsar's surface probably give off these radio beams. A pulsar has a very strong magnetic field which may speed up these high energy particles.

Pulsars are thought to be neutron stars. Neutron stars are small but extremely dense (thick) stars made up of tightly compressed neutrons. (*See* DENSITY.) The diameter of a neutron star is only a few kilometers or miles. Neutron stars form when a large star collapses inward on itself during a supernova explosion. (*See* SUPERNOVA.)

The most famous pulsar is in the Crab Nebula. The supernova explosion that formed the Crab Nebula was recorded by the Chinese in A.D. 1054. The pulsar of the Crab Nebula spins about 30 times per second, although the rate is lessening by about 15 microseconds a year. Astronomers think that the pulsars that give off rapid pulses are younger than those that give off slower pulses. *See also* NEUTRON STAR; STAR.   J.M.C./C.R.

PULSE (pəls′) The pulse is the wave of pressure that passes through the body's arteries every time the heart contracts (draws together) to pump the blood. The pulse can be felt by placing fingers on the wrist above the thumb at a point over the radial artery. Pulse can also be felt by touching the temples where the temporal artery is located and at other locations on the body where an artery (a branching tube that carries blood from the heart to parts of the body) is near the surface.

Pulse cannot be felt in the veins because blood reaches them from the arteries by passing through the narrow capillaries. The capillaries lessen the pressure and even out its variations.

The pulse rate of a child is faster than that of the average healthy adult. Older people often have a slow pulse rate. The pulse rate for a normal man is 72 beats per minute. The pulse rate of the average woman is usually 76 to 80 beats per minute. The normal rate for a seven-year-old child is 90 beats per minute. A newborn baby can have a pulse rate of 140. Older adults can be in the 50-65 range of pulse rate. *See also* ARTERY; HEART. W.R.P./J.J.F.

PUMA (pü′ mə) The puma (*Felis concolor*) is a large, wild mammal belonging to the cat family. Pumas are widely divided throughout the Americas, from Canada to Patagonia (southward to the tip of South America). These animals can live in deserts, mountains, or forests.

The puma is called by several other names, including mountain lion, cougar, catamount, and (in some areas) panther. The name "panther" is also given to several other types of cats. The puma generally looks like a female African lion.

An adult puma may be either gray, reddish, or yellowish (tawny) in color. Some pumas are solid black. A full grown puma may be 1.5 m [5 ft] long, not including its long tail. The females have from one to six cubs (babies) at a time. Litters (young born at one time) are usually two years apart.

Though the puma has a soft whistle, the animal is better known for its wild cry. The cry sounds like a person screaming in fright.

Pumas often hunt at night. The animals are famous for their stamina (ability to survive) and strength, covering great distances while hunting. The puma's main food is deer. Pumas often carry their victims slung over their backs. Because pumas feed often on old and diseased deer, biologists believe pumas play an important part in the animal world. *See* CARBON CYCLE; FOOD CHAIN.

J.J.A./J.J.M.

The puma (above) is a large, wild mammal which can live in deserts, mountains, or forests. Pumas are famous for their great stamina and strength. They cover great distances while hunting.

PUMICE (pəm′ əs) Pumice is a light, gray-colored rock containing many tiny holes. It is used for polishing, scouring, and scrubbing, either as a powder or in pieces. In the home, pieces of pumice are sometimes used for removing stains or calluses (hard skin) from the hands. These pieces are known as pumice stone.

Pumice is formed by volcanoes. When a volcano erupts, it throws out molten lava. (*See* VOLCANO.) Pumice is formed when acidic lava cools and solidifies or hardens

Some different kinds of pumps are shown here. 1) Vacuum pump. Steam enters the pipe and passes through a narrow section perforated with holes. The narrowing causes a reduction in pressure and air from the tank is sucked into the pipe. The air and steam mixture leaves the pipe, and air is gradually pumped out of the tank. 2) Centrifugal pump. The fluid being pumped is fed to the center of a set of revolving blades. It is flung outward by the blades and discharged. 3) Gear pump. The fluid is fed in, carried round by the gear wheels and pushed out at the other side of the casing. 4) Lift pump. As the handle is pushed down, the piston goes up and the pressure of the air outside forces water into the cylinder through a valve at the bottom. The water is sucked up into the space left by the piston. The handle is pulled up and the water flows through a valve in the piston. The handle is pushed down again, the piston rises, and the valve in the piston closes. This pushes the water to the spout of the pump, while more water fills the space below the piston.

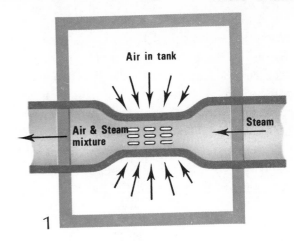

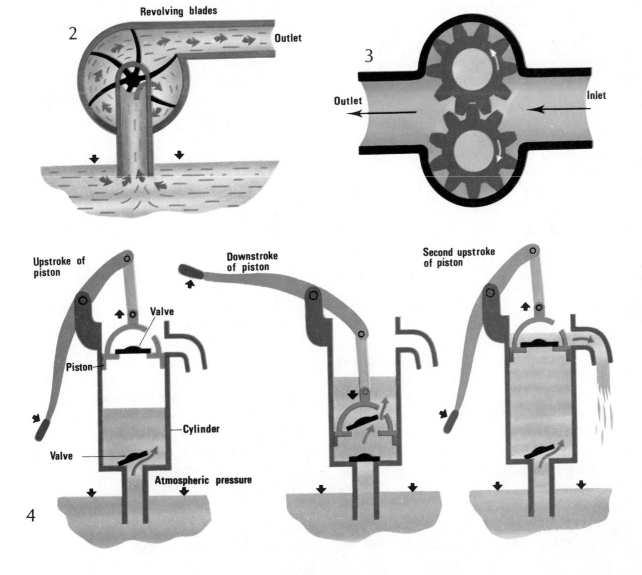

very quickly. Lava contains volcanic gases. When it cools quickly, the gases become trapped in the lava. This is how the bubbles are formed in pumice. Because it has so many holes, pumice is so light that it usually floats on water. Sometimes solid lumps of pumice are blown out of volcanoes during explosions. This happened during the famous Krakatoa explosion in 1883. Sailors reported seeing large masses of pumice floating on the ocean.

M.E./W.R.S.

PUMP (pəmp′) A pump is a machine that is used for transferring fluids from one point to another. A fluid can be either a gas or a liquid. There are three main kinds of pump—the reciprocating pump, the rotary pump, and the centrifugal pump.

The simplest reciprocating pump is a bicycle pump. A bicycle pump has a piston—a cylinder that moves back and forth inside a larger cylinder—which is attached to a handle. As the piston is pulled up the cylinder, air is sucked in through a valve. Then the piston is pushed back down the cylinder. The force of the air closes the valve and the air is pumped into the tire. This is called a single-acting pump. Some reciprocating pumps have a valve on each side of the piston. Then the piston pumps fluid when it is moving in either direction. This produces a more even flow of fluid. This is called a double-acting pump. Another example of a reciprocating pump is the lift pump. This is the type of pump used for pumping water from wells.

In a rotary pump, the fluid is transferred by a rotary (turning on an axis like a wheel) device. An example of the rotary pump is the gear pump. A gear pump contains two gear wheels that interlock. These wheels turn round inside a casing. The fluid is carried round the gears in the spaces between the teeth. In this way, the fluid is transferred from one side of the gears to the other. The gear pump works well for heavy liquids but not for gases. Gear pumps are widely used in the petroleum industry. Other kinds of rotary pumps use spinning blades instead of gear wheels.

Centrifugal pumps contain a fan-shaped device called an impeller. The impeller spins round very fast and fluid is fed into the middle of it. The fluid is then flung outward by the vanes of the impeller into the chamber. Usually centrifugal pumps contain a number of impellers, perhaps 20 or more.

These three main kinds of pump can pump either liquids or gases. However, the design of a gas pump is slightly different from that of a liquid pump. Gas pumps must work at a higher speed. Also, the various parts have to fit together better to prevent leaks.

Another kind of pump is the vacuum pump. They are widely used in industry for emptying containers of fluid. When a fluid flows through a pipe, it travels faster where the pipe narrows. When a fluid travels faster, its pressure decreases. Therefore the pressure of a fluid decreases when it flows through a narrower pipe. This is how a vacuum pump works. Steam enters a pipe and then flows into a narrow section. The narrow part of the pipe contains many tiny holes. As the steam flows through the narrow section, its pressure decreases. This causes the fluid to be sucked in through the small holes. In this way, the fluid is pumped out of the container. M.E./J.T.

PUPA (pyü′ pə) The pupa is the nonfeeding, usually nonmoving stage in the development of those insects that belong to the more advanced orders. The pupal stage follows the larval stage in complete metamorphosis. (*See* METAMORPHOSIS.) The pupa makes special hormones which cause it to develop into an adult (imago). While in the pupal stage, the insect develops structures, such as wings, that are characteristic of the adult. In many insects, the pupa is enclosed in a case or cocoon. This case may be made of silk or some other substance. When fully developed, the pupa breaks open the case and comes out as an

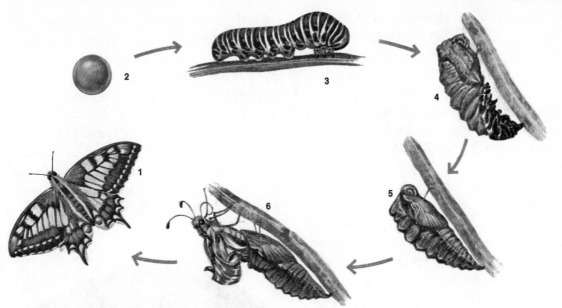

The pupa is one of the stages of the metamorphosis of a butterfly. The adult (1) lays an egg (2) which develops into a larva (3). The larva forms a cocoon (4) around itself and becomes a pupa (5) from which the adult emerges (6).

adult. The pupa of a butterfly or moth is also called a chrysalis. *See also* BUTTERFLY AND MOTH; HORMONE; INSECT; LARVA.

A.J.C./J.E.R.

PURSLANE FAMILY The purslane (pər' slən) family includes 15 genera and 250 species of annual and perennial herbaceous plants. They are all dicotyledons. The leaves are simple and fleshy. The flowers have no petals but do have two to six colored sepals. Each flower also has five stamens and two or three pistils. (*See* FLOWER.)

Members of the genus *Portulaca* are able to withstand unfavorable environmental conditions. They grow in almost any type of soil. One species (*Portulaca oleracea*) is a weed that is disliked by farmers and gardeners throughout North America. It is frequently called pussley or purslane. This weed covers large areas and multiplies very quickly. It covers the ground with such a thick growth that it kills other plants and gives shelter to harmful insects. *See also* WEED.

A.J.C./M.H.S.

PVC PVC is one of the most widely used of all plastics. Its full name is polyvinyl chloride (päl' ē vīn' əl klōr' īd'). Plastics are made by a process called polymerization. In polymerization, large numbers of small molecules are linked together to form a long, chainlike molecule. The long chain molecule is called a polymer. (*See* POLYMERIZATION.) PVC is made by linking up molecules of vinyl chloride (CH_2-CHCl). This is done by vigorously mixing vinyl chloride with water. This breaks up the vinyl chloride into tiny droplets. Then a catalyst is added. The catalyst polymerizes the vinyl chloride into PVC. Sometimes molecules of vinyl chloride are linked with molecules of vinyl acetate. This is called copolymerization. This gives a plastic that is strong and adhesive.

By itself, PVC is rather brittle. A substance called a plasticizer is added to make it flexible. Flexible PVC is used to make raincoats, boots, and upholstery. If only a small amount of plasticizer is added, then the PVC is more rigid (hard). Rigid PVC is used to make pipes, roofing sheets, and long-playing records. PVC is very resistant to weathering and is also a very good insulator for electricity. For this reason, it has largely replaced rubber for insulating electrical wiring. It is not attacked by either acids or alkalis and so is used for pipes in the chemical industry.

M.E./A.D.

PYRAMID (pir′ ə mid′) A pyramid is a large stone structure with a square base and four triangular-shaped sides that come to a point at the top. In ancient times, people used pyramids as tombs or temples. The most famous pyramids are those built around 4,500 years ago as tombs for Egyptian kings. Pyramids can also be found in Central and South America. The Egyptian pyramids are considered to be among the Seven Wonders of the Ancient World.

The ruins of 35 pyramids still stand along the Nile River in Egypt. They were built to protect the bodies of Egyptian kings. The bodies were mummified (dried and wrapped in cloth) for preservation and placed in secret chambers, or rooms, filled with gold and treasure. Passageways connected various other burial chambers inside the pyramid.

Some pyramids rise in a series of giant steps. Others have smooth sides. The pyramid of Khufu, called the Great Pyramid, contains more than 2 million stone blocks that average 2.3 metric tons [2.5 tons] each. The pyramid was originally 147 m [481 ft] tall, but some stones have fallen off and it is now about 137 m [450 ft] high. Its base covers about 5 hectares [13 acres].

The pyramids are a miracle of building skill. The ancient Egyptians had no machinery or iron tools. The huge blocks were cut out of limestone quarries with copper chisels and saws. They were then dragged many miles across the desert by gangs of men. More than 400,000 men worked each year for 20 years to build the Great Pyramid. When the first layer of blocks was in place, ramps were built so that blocks could be dragged to upper layers.

The Indians of Central and South America built pyramids that had flat tops. The flat tops served as bases for their temples. The pyramid built by the Toltec Indians near Cholula, Mexico, is one of the largest pyramids in the world. Other well-known pyramids are located near Mexico City, Mexico, and in Peru.

The pyramid is also a shape in geometry. The base can have any number of sides, and this determines how many triangular side faces there are. A pyramid with three equilateral sides is called a tetrahedron.

W.R.P./R.W.L.

The Pyramid of the Sun, shown above, is in Teotihuacan, Mexico.

PYRITE (pī′ rīt′) Pyrite is a brassy-yellow colored mineral made of iron and sulfur. Because of its color, pyrite is often mistaken for gold, and has been given the nickname, "fool's gold." Pyrite may be distinguished from gold by its much higher degree of hardness and brittleness. Pyrite may have been used by prehistoric man to make fire.

Pyrite is an important source of sulfuric acid. Large deposits of pyrite are found in Spain, the United States, Italy, and Norway. *See also* MINERAL.

J.M.C./R.H.

PYROMETER (pī räm′ ət ər) A pyrometer is an instrument that is used for measuring high temperatures. It is used, for example, to measure the temperature in a furnace. There are two main kinds of pyrometers: the radiation pyrometer and the optical pyrometer.

In a radiation pyrometer, heat is concentrated by a lens onto a device such as a thermocouple. When a thermocouple is heated, it produces a voltage. (*See* THERMOCOUPLE.) The size of the voltage depends on the temperature. Sometimes a bolometer is used instead of a thermocouple. A bolometer has two strips of the metal platinum. When the platinum strips heat up, the electrical resistance of the strips changes. The change of resistance can be used to measure the temperature.

Optical pyrometers use the light coming from a hot object to measure its temperature. The brightness and color of the light change with the temperature of the object. The light is compared to the light from a tungsten filament lamp. The filament is seen against a background of light from the object. The voltage through the filament is varied. The changing voltage heats or cools the filament and makes it brighter or dimmer. At a certain voltage, the filament disappears in the background because the two colors are the same. The size of the voltage through the filament can be used to measure the temperature.   M.E./R.W.L.

PYTHAGOREAN THEOREM (pə thag′ ə rē′ ən thē′ ə rəm)

The Pythagorean theorem is a theorem in geometry that states that the square of the length of the hypotenuse of a right triangle equals the sum of the squares of the lengths of the other two sides. A right-angled triangle is a triangle that contains a right angle. The longest side in a right-angled triangle is the one opposite the right angle. This side is called the hypotenuse. A simple right-angled triangle has sides of length 3, 4, and 5. The longest side is 5 units long, so this is the hypotenuse. Its square is 25 (5 × 5). The square of 3 is 9 and the square of 4 is 16. 9 + 16 = 25 and therefore the Pythagorean theorem is correct.

The Pythagorean theorem is named after the great Greek mathematician and philosopher Pythagoras. He lived from about 580 to 500 B.C. However, he probably did not invent the theory himself. It is more likely that it was discovered by one of his followers after his death.   M.E./S.P.A.

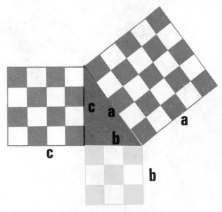

According to the Pythagorean theorem: if *a* is the length of the longest side of the triangle, and the lengths of the other sides are *b* and *c* respectively, then the theorem can be written $a^2 = b^2 + c^2$.

PYTHON (pī′ thän′)

Python is a genus of 20–25 species of large, non-venomous snakes belonging to the family Boidae. They are native to the tropical rain forests of Africa, Asia, and Australia. Most live near the water, and are able to swim and climb well. Pythons are related to the boas (*See* BOA.). Unlike the boas, however, pythons are oviparous. This means that they lay eggs which hatch in a nest. A female python lays 15–100 eggs at a time, depending on her size. She then coils herself around the eggs and incubates them (keeps them warm) for 60–80 days. This is very unusual behavior for a snake, particularly when one considers that snakes are ectothermic (cold blooded animals). The body temperature of a cold blooded animal is usually about the same as the temperature of its surroundings. Due to this incubation, however, the temperature of the eggs remains about 10°C [18°F] higher than that of the surroundings.

A python kills its prey by wrapping itself in coils around the victim and squeezing it to death. By tightening its coils, the python cuts off a victim's circulation and breathing. The python then swallows the dead victim whole.

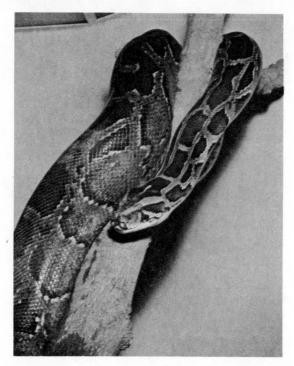

The python (above) is a large snake found in Africa, Asia, and Australia.

sea for measuring latitudes (the distance north or south of the equator measured in degrees). Quadrants were also used by astronomers for finding the positions of stars. A quadrant was made of a strip of metal shaped like a quarter of a circle. The strip had a scale marked on it from 0° to 90°. At each end of the strip there were two more strips of metal. They were joined to each other where the middle of the circle would be. At this joint, a lead weight hung on the end of a cord. Sometimes the weight hung from a strip of metal. Along one side of the quadrant there were two holes. The navigator would line up these two holes with the Pole Star (the star toward which the northern end of the earth's axis very nearly points). Someone else would read aloud where the weighted cord passed across the scale. This gave the angle of the Pole Star above the horizon. This angle was the same as the latitude at that point. *See also* NAVIGATION.

M.E./C.R.

During the next few days, the python hardly moves at all as it digests its meal. (*See* DIGESTION.)

The largest python is the reticulated python (*Python reticulatus*). It may reach 9.6 m [31.5 ft] long and weigh 115 kg [254 lb]. It rivals the giant anaconda of South America as the world's largest snake. Some reticulated pythons prey on small goats, pigs, and deer, but they usually prefer smaller animals.

The Indian python (*Python morulus*) and the African python (*Python sebae*) are smaller, usually less than 7 m [23 ft] long. They prey on small animals and rodents, and are considered helpful in many areas where they live.

A.J.C./R.L.L.

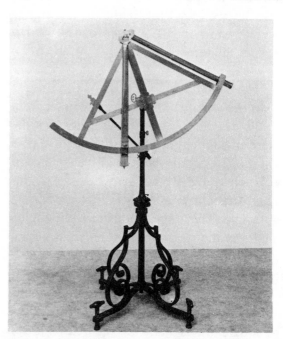

The quadrant (above) is an instrument which was used to measure latitude and altitude.

QUADRANT (kwäd′ rənt) The quadrant is an instrument that was used by navigators at

QUAIL (kwāl′) A quail is a small, chunky, chickenlike bird that belongs to the family Phasianidae. It is closely related to the partridge, pheasant, grouse, and turkey. (*See* GROUSE; PHEASANT.) There are seven species of quail in North America. They grow from 17.5 to 25 cm [7 to 10 in] long. The feathers of the quail are mostly brown, black, and gray in color. The quail's beak is short and stubby. It is used to pick seeds, berries, and insects off of the ground. Quails live in fields and open country. They are popular game birds. One well-known quail is the bobwhite; its name sounds like its call. S.R.G./L.L.S.

QUANTA (kwänt′ ə) Quanta is the plural of quantum, which is a very small quantity into which many forms of energy are subdivided. The word quanta was first used by the German physicist Max Planck in 1900. In order to explain a certain property of light, he regarded it as consisting of particles instead of waves. Previously, scientists had thought that all properties of light could be explained by regarding it as a wave motion. Planck called these particles of light quanta.

Today, the word is commonly used in nuclear and particle physics. It now has a wider meaning. It refers to any quantity that can have only certain values. For example, there exist hundreds of kinds of tiny particles called elementary or subatomic particles. Atoms consist of three different elementary particles: protons, neutrons, and electrons. Some of these particles spin rather in the same way as a ball spins when it is thrown. The spin can be ½ a unit, or 1, 1 ½, 2, and so on. But it cannot be ⅔ or ¼ of a unit. The spin is said to be quantized, because only these certain spin units are possible. M.E./J.T.

QUANTUM THEORY (kwänt′ əm thē′ ə rē) Quantum theory is a theory in physics based on the general idea of the subdivision of radiant energy into finite quanta and applied to several processes including transference or transformation of energy in an atomic or molecular scale. At the end of the 1800s, physicists considered light as a wave motion.

This theory of light explained almost all of its properties. However, there were many effects that could not be explained. One of these effects was that hot objects give off visible light. For example, a red-hot object gives off mostly red light. The frequency (rate of occurrence) of the light given off depends only on the temperature. The frequency does not depend on the substance out of which the object is made. The wave theory of light tried to explain how the frequency depends on the temperature. However, the theory failed at the frequencies of ultraviolet light. (*See* ULTRAVIOLET LIGHT.) This failure was known as the ultraviolet catastrophe.

The problem was solved in 1900 by a German physicist, Max Planck. (*See* PLANCK, MAX.) He suggested that the light is given off in packets. He called a packet of light a quantum. His theory explained exactly how the frequency changes with the temperature. His theory was known as the quantum theory. In Max Planck's theory, the energy of each quantum is proportional to its frequency. This can be written as $E = hf$. Here, E is the energy, f is the frequency, and h is a constant. It is called Planck's constant and is very small indeed. It is equal to 6.6256×10^{-34} joule seconds. (*See* PLANCK'S CONSTANT.)

In 1905 the quantum theory solved another problem. When light falls on certain substances, they sometimes give off electrons from their atoms. This is called the photoelectric effect. (*See* PHOTOELECTRIC EFFECT.) The light has to be above a certain frequency. The wave theory could not explain why light had to be above a certain frequency. However, this was explained in 1905 by the great physicist Albert Einstein. He explained it by using Planck's quantum theory. (*See* EINSTEIN, ALBERT.) He also named the particles of light photons. (*See* PHOTON.)

The next step in the development of the quantum theory came in 1913. In that year, a Danish physicist Niels Bohr worked out the first theory of the atom. (*See* BOHR, NIELS.)

By using the quantum theory, he managed to produce a fairly accurate model of the atom. (*See* ATOM.)

Now physicists did not know whether light was made up of waves or particles. The wave theory was still needed to explain effects such as the diffraction of light. (*See* DIFFRACTION.) However, in certain experiments, light certainly behaved as if it were made up of particles. The situation became even more complicated in 1924. In that year a French physicist, Louis de Broglie, suggested that electrons could behave like waves. Before this, electrons were thought of as particles. Two years later a new theory of the atom was produced by a German physicist Erwin Schrödinger. (*See* SCHRÖDINGER, ERWIN.) Calling his theory wave mechanics, Schrödinger developed an equation for describing the wave properties of electrons. Solutions of this equation were expressed by four values, known as quantum numbers. These numbers helped physicists to describe the energy state of an electron. Using quantum numbers, in 1925 the Austrian physicist Wolfgang Pauli developed a principle for determining how many electrons can occupy each electron shell of any atom.

At the same time that Schrödinger introduced his theory, another German physicist, Werner Heisenberg, produced a different theory, using mathematical devices called matrices. (*See* MATRIX.) His theory was called matrix mechanics. Later, Schrödinger succeeded in showing that wave mechanics and matrix mechanics are different mathematical approaches to the same theory, which became known as quantum mechanics. Finally, Heisenberg's uncertainty principle helped to show that waves and particles are complementary properties of electromagnetic radiation. Thus, particles can behave like waves under the right conditions. For example, photons and electrons can collide (strike against each other) with other particles. A wave could never take part in a colli-sion. However, photons and electrons cannot behave like waves and particles at the same time. They always behave like one or the other.

Since the 1920s, the quantum theory has enabled physicists to understand many aspects of the atomic world. For example, magnetism is now fairly well understood. This would not have been possible without quantum theory. Quantum theory is also used in solid state physics. Solid state physics is the branch of physics that studies solids. (*See* SOLID STATE PHYSICS.) Quantum theory explains the properties of solids in terms of their atoms. Quantum theory has enabled physicists to understand how transistors work. (*See* TRANSITOR.) Quantum theory is also an important tool for understanding the subatomic world. With it physicists now understand many properties of the nucleus and of radioactivity. *See also* ATOMIC NUCLEUS; RADIOACTIVITY.   M.E./J.T.

QUARK (kwärk′) A quark is a hypothetical (assumed to be true) particle that carries a fractional electric charge and that is believed to be a constituent (ingredient) of known elementary particles. All matter is made up of small particles called atoms. Atoms consist of a central core, called a nucleus, surrounded by electrons. This was discovered early in the 20th century. Then physicists found that the nucleus itself has a structure. It is made up of particles called protons and neutrons. (*See* NUCLEUS, ATOMIC.) These three particles—protons, neutrons, and electrons—are known as subatomic or elementary particles. Physicists have since discovered hundreds of other elementary particles.

In 1964 two American physicists, Murray Gell-Mann and George Zweig, suggested that many elementary particles might also have a structure. They suggested that the group of elementary particles called hadrons might also have a structure. (*See* PARTICLE PHYSICS.) There are probably six different kinds of

The crane in the center is used to lift and break up limestone in this quarry in Pennsylvania.

quark, each having an antiparticle called an antiquark. (*See* ANTIMATTER.) Different combinations of these quarks give rise to different elementary particles. There are only a few particles that are not made up of quarks. These are the photon and the leptons—the electron, the muon, and the neutrino.

Many elementary particles have an electric charge. The size of their charge is always the same as the size of the charge on the proton and electron. If the particles contain a number of quarks, then quarks must have a fraction of this charge. Physicists have looked for quarks by trying to find particles with a fractional charge. So far they have not found any.   M.E./J.T.

QUARRYING (kwȯr′ ē ing) Quarrying is a process by which stone is taken out of the ground. The pit, or excavation, from which the stone is to be taken is called a quarry. The type of stone and the way it is to be used determine the method of quarrying.

Granite is difficult to quarry because of its hardness. Granite is usually quarried by the plug-and-feather method. In this process, a series of small holes are drilled into the rock. Then two semicircular pieces of steel, called feathers, are put in each hole. A steel wedge (plug) is forced between the feathers. The plugs and feathers are then driven into the ground, splitting the rock. Further splitting can often be done by using smaller tools.

Very sophisticated methods are used to quarry marble. First, a sample of marble is obtained by a machine that drills a deep hole into the deposit. A cylinder is taken out from which experts can decide how deep below the surface the best marble is. Grooves are then cut in lines at right angles to each other, forming blocks. The blocks are loosened and taken out by drilling or by the plug-and-feather method.

Stratified (layered) rock is fairly easy to quarry. Sandstone, slate, and limestone are often quarried by simple drilling or prying. Weak explosives are often used. Stronger explosives are used when broken stone is required for road building.

Stone is quarried throughout the world. Some 6,000 quarries in the United States produce 610 million metric tons [1 billion tons] of stone a year.   J.M.C./R.H.

QUARTZ (kwȯrts′) Quartz is a hard, glossy mineral made of silicon and oxygen. Its chem-

The photograph above shows rock crystal, or pure quartz. Below right are six-sided quartz crystals seen with a copper-iron sulfide, chalcopyrite.

ical formula is SiO_2. Quartz breaks much like glass and is common in almost all types of rock.

Pure quartz, called rock crystal, is made entirely of silicon and oxygen. It has a transparent glassy appearance and is used mainly for jewelry. Impure quartz crystals include amethyst, a purple-colored quartz, and citrine, a golden yellow variety. Noncrystalline quartz, including jasper and flint, is made of many fine grains instead of large single crystals.

Quartz has many electronic uses because of its piezoelectric nature. (*See* PIEZOELECTRIC EFFECT.) This property of quartz allows the generation of voltage across the crystal when it is deformed. Because of this effect, electric signals can be changed into sound

waves, and vice versa. The piezoelectric effect of quartz plays an important role in radios, television, radar, and clocks.

Quartz has many other important uses. It is used to make glass and lenses which will transmit ultraviolet light. It is also used as an abrasive in sandpaper. *See also* MINERAL.

J.M.C./R.H.

QUARTZITE (kwȯrt′ sīt′) Quartzite is a rock made of quartz grains cemented together by silica. When split, the quartz crystals as well as the cement split, giving two smooth surfaces.

Quartzite is formed from sandstone in which the quartz crystals have recrystallized. This recrystallization can be caused by heat and pressure, resulting in a kind of quartzite called metaquartzite. Recrystallization can also be caused by silica-laden water, producing a quartzite called orthoquartzite. *See also* QUARTZ.

J.M.C./R.H.

QUASAR (kwā′ zär′) Quasars (quasi-stellar radio sources) were first discovered in 1960. Radio astronomers noticed very strong radio signals coming from certain parts of the sky. They measured their positions in the sky. Then astronomers looked at photographs of those parts of the sky and saw what seemed to be faint blue stars.

Many astronomers believe that quasars are very far away. It is believed that the universe is expanding because all the stars and galaxies seem to be moving away from us. The further away the stars and galaxies are, the faster they are traveling. Quasars seem to be moving very fast indeed. Therefore some astronomers think that they must be very far away. However, if they are very far away, then they must be giving out huge amounts of energy. Otherwise, we would not be able to detect them. The energy that quasars give out is hundreds of times more than the energy that our galaxy produces. There is another strange fact about quasars. Their energy varies over a

few weeks or months. This could happen only if they were at least a million times smaller than our own galaxy.

It may be that quasars are not as far away as some astronomers think. Some quasars seem to be associated with certain galaxies. These galaxies are not as far away as the quasars seem to be. If this were true, their brightness would not be so unusual. Some astronomers now think that quasars are very young galaxies.

M.E./C.R.

QUATERNARY PERIOD (kwät′ ə ner′ ē pir′ ē əd) The Quaternary period began about 2 million years ago and extends to the present. It is divided into the Pleistocene epoch and the Recent (Holocene) epoch.

During the Quarternary, modern people emerged and dominated the earth. They domesticated animals and cultivated plants. The early part of the Quaternary saw the extinction of most large mammals. The modern species adapted to their respective ecosystems.

The major climatic event of the Quaternary was the Pleistocene ice ages. These periods of glaciation shaped the landscape of the northern regions. Some geologists believe that the Recent epoch is actually an interglacial (between ice ages) period. *See also* GEOLOGICAL TIME SCALE; GLACIATION; PLEISTOCENE EPOCH; RECENT EPOCH.

J.M.C./W.R.S.

QUICKSAND (kwik′ sand′) Quicksand is a fine, powdery sand saturated (soaked) with water. It is found on the bottoms of brooks and streams, and along the seashore.

Saturated quicksand cannot hold very much weight. A person may drown while trying to walk on quicksand. Instead of struggling, a person who falls into quicksand should try to float on top of it. J.M.C./W.R.S.

QUININE (kwī′ nīn′) Quinine is a bitter substance that is taken from the bark of the cinchona tree. Cinchona trees grow mainly in South America, India, and Indonesia.

Quinine is used mainly in treating diseases, especially malaria. The drug lowers the fever during malaria attacks, but does not cure the disease. Quinine is used to treat malaria in many tropical regions where the drug is cheap and easy to obtain.

In the United States, quinine has largely been replaced by synthetic drugs. But many doctors still use the drug quinidine to treat certain disorders of heart rhythm. Quinidine has the same chemical formula as quinine but differs from it in the way the atoms are arranged in the molecule.

Doctors believe quinine and quinidine may cause abnormalities in unborn children. Pregnant women, therefore, should not take these drugs without first checking with a physician. *See also* MALARIA.   J.J.A./J.J.F.

Quinine is extracted from the bark (above) of Cinchona trees which grow mainly in South America, India, and Indonesia. Quinine is used especially for treating malaria in many tropical regions where the drug is cheap and easy to obtain.

RABBIT (rab′ ət) Rabbits are small, furry mammals that, along with hares, belong to the family Leporidae. (*See* HARE.) Wild rabbits are usually brown or gray. They are about 35 cm [14 in] long and weigh about 2.5 kg [5.5 lb]. Pet rabbits may be any of several colors. They are larger than wild rabbits, often reaching a length of 55 cm [22 in] and a weight of 5 kg [11 lb]. Rabbits have small, furry tails. They have a keen sense of smell and are able to move their ears to "catch" even faint sounds.

Rabbits usually live in underground tunnels, called burrows, or in shallow holes called forms. Frequently, these burrows and forms have been dug and abandoned by other animals. Although rabbits commonly live alone, they may form communities and live in warrens. A warren is a group of burrows that have been dug close together. Each warren is ruled by a dominant male, or buck. (*See* DOMINANCE.)

Rabbits are peaceful, nonaggressive animals. If threatened, a rabbit may try to hide by staying perfectly still. A frightened rabbit can hop farther than 3 m [10 ft]. It can move faster than 30 km [18 mi] per hour. A rabbit tires easily, however, and may try to outwit an enemy by running in a circular or zigzag pattern.

Rabbits usually sleep during the day, and eat and play at night. (*See* NOCTURNAL HABIT.) They are herbivores and eat almost any kind of plant. Some rabbits cause extensive crop damage and are considered to be pests.

After mating and a gestation period of about a month, a female rabbit gives birth to a litter of two to nine kits. Some rabbits have more than five litters a year. The mother stays near her kits and feeds them for about two weeks. She covers them with grass and with fur from her own chest. After two weeks, the kits leave the form and dig new ones of their own.

The two major kinds of rabbits are the cottontails, or New World rabbits (genus *Sylvilagus*), and the European, or Old World rabbits (genus *Oryctolagus*). Cottontails live in North and South America, from Canada to Argentina and Paraguay. European rabbits are native to Europe and northern Africa. They have since been introduced into many other countries. Where there are no natural enemies, the rabbits reproduce rapidly. They are considered to be major pests in Australia, New Zealand, and South America. Some of the natural enemies of rabbits include birds of prey, cats, dogs, coyotes, foxes, minks, weasels, and wolves. Human beings, however, are the greatest enemies of rabbits. They hunt rabbits for their skin, fur, and meat. In areas where they are pests, rabbits are poisoned or trapped in great numbers. *See also* BIOLOGICAL CONTROL; MAMMAL.

A.J.C./J.J.M.

Shown above is an eastern cottontail rabbit.

RABIES (rā′ bēz) Rabies is a disease that infects the brain and spinal cord. The disease, which almost always causes death, destroys the nerve cells of part of the brain. The infection is caused by a virus that lives in the saliva of a carrier (called a host). Most mammals can carry the virus. If the host bites a human being or animal, the victim may get rabies. The virus can enter mucous membranes (such as the lining of the nose), but it cannot enter unbroken skin.

In human beings, symptoms of rabies include pain, a burning feeling, or numbness where the infection occurred. Rabies is also called hydrophobia, which means "fear of water." Sometimes the sight of water creates painful throat contractions. After a day or two, a quiet period occurs, followed by unconsciousness and death. The disease lasts from three to twelve days.

Dogs infected with rabies bark and growl constantly. They often attack without reason. Some infected dogs do not go mad but show signs of paralysis, called "dumb rabies." Paralysis of the throat and jaw are common.

Any person bitten by an animal should wash the wound immediately with soap and water and see a doctor. The animal should be penned and watched to see if it shows any symptoms of rabies. If such symptoms occur, the person who was bitten should be vaccinated at once. Formerly, rabies vaccine had to be given in daily injections for a period of from two to four weeks. In the 1970s, a new, safer vaccine was developed that requires fewer injections. *See also* PASTEUR, LOUIS.

J.J.A./J.J.F.

RACCOON (ra kün′) The raccoon is a furry mammal belonging to the same family as lesser pandas, kinkajous, and ringtails. Raccoons are found throughout North, Central, and South America.

The raccoon is usually gray in color, sometimes tinged with yellow or brown. It has a bushy, ringed tail, and is especially noted for a band of black hair around its eyes that resembles a mask. Raccoons have pointed snouts and strong, sharp claws. The

The raccoon (above) is a furry mammal.

animals use their paws to find food. They can handle objects almost as skillfully as monkeys.

There are two main species of raccoons. The northern raccoon (*Procyon lotor*) lives in Canada, the United States, and Central America. It measures from 76 to 97 cm [30 to 38 in] in length, including the tail. Males are generally larger than females. The crab-eating raccoon (*Procyon cancrivorous*) lives in South America. This type of raccoon has shorter hair and longer legs than the northern raccoon.

Raccoons live both on the ground and in trees. They may live alone or in small family groups. Each raccoon has a home range. Within this range, which may cover 81 hectares [200 acres], the raccoon mates, builds its home, and searches for food. Raccoons usually hunt for food at night. They eat a variety of foods, such as crabs, crayfish, frogs, fish, acorns, corn, fruit, grasshoppers, and mice.

Northern raccoons mate once a year between January and June. About nine weeks after mating, the female has from one to seven babies. J.J.A./J.J.M.

RADAR

Radar (rā′ där) is a method of detecting objects that are far away by using radio waves. The word radar stands for radio detection and ranging. Radar works on the same principle that bats use when they fly at night. As a bat flies, it lets out a series of short squeaks. These squeaks are very high-pitched and humans cannot hear them. If there is an object in the path of the bat, the sound wave hits it and is reflected back. The bat can hear the reflections and so detect the object.

Radar works in a very similar manner. Instead of sound waves, radio waves are used. The radar sends out short pulses of radio waves. If they hit an object, they are reflected back from it. The reflected wave is called the echo and can be detected by the radar equipment. The time taken for the echo to be picked up depends on how far away the object is. This allows the distance of the object to be calculated. Usually the radar equipment has a screen. The echo is shown as a bright spot on the screen. The screen has a scale marked on it to indicate the direction and distance of the object.

How radar works Most radar sends out a series of pulses. This type of radar is called a pulse radar. The radar set contains a device called a modulator. This sends out a series of electronic pulses to a transmitter. The transmitter contains a vacuum tube called a multi-cavity magnetron. When a current passes through a magnetron, it gives out very short wavelength radio waves. Therefore, when the modulator gives out a pulse, the magnetron sends out a burst of radio waves. The wavelength of these waves is between 1 and 10 cms [0.5 to 5 in]. These waves are called microwaves. There are about a thousand pulses given out in a minute. Each pulse lasts for only a millionth of a second. The microwaves are fed into an antenna. The antenna then transmits the waves through the air. Surrounding the antenna is a device called a reflector. The radio waves from the antenna are reflected off the reflector and are focused in a particular direction. Some reflectors are

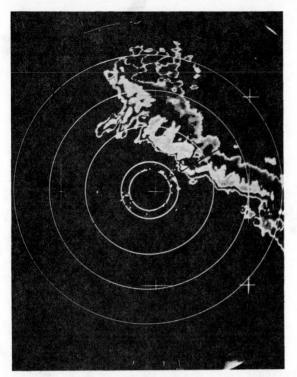

Weather radar can spot turbulent thunderclouds up to 80 km [50 mi] away. Radar can tell the difference between the small raindrops of an ordinary cloud and the large drops of a thundercloud.

Delicate radar aerials are protected from the weather by domes (above), called radomes. The domes do not affect the electromagnetic waves.

shaped like a trough. Others are dish-shaped or funnel-shaped.

The antenna and reflector are mounted on a turntable called the scanner. The scanner rotates, usually 10 to 25 times a minute. Sometimes the radar can scan much more quickly than this. For example, some radars are designed to detect missiles. These radars can scan the sky in a few millionths of a second.

If the radar beam hits an object, part of the beam is reflected back to the radar set. It is then picked up by an instrument called the receiver. The receiver strengthens, or amplifies, the beam. (*See* AMPLIFIER.) The beam is converted into an electronic signal. This is then fed into a device called a cathode-ray tube. (*See* CATHODE-RAY TUBE.) The cathode-ray tube contains a screen called an indicator screen or an indicator. The signal is converted into a bright spot on the indicator screen.

There are several different kinds of indicator. The most widely used is the plain position indicator, or PPI. This indicator shows both the position and the direction of the object. The indicator has a line like the radius of a circle, from the middle of the screen to the outer edge. This line sweeps around the central point on the screen. It rotates every time that the scanner rotates. The screen has a pattern of rings marked on it. They are used to

A yacht radar set is shown above. Many yachts and ships are equipped with radar sets to help navigation and to detect storm clouds. By using radar, ships can sail when visibility is bad.

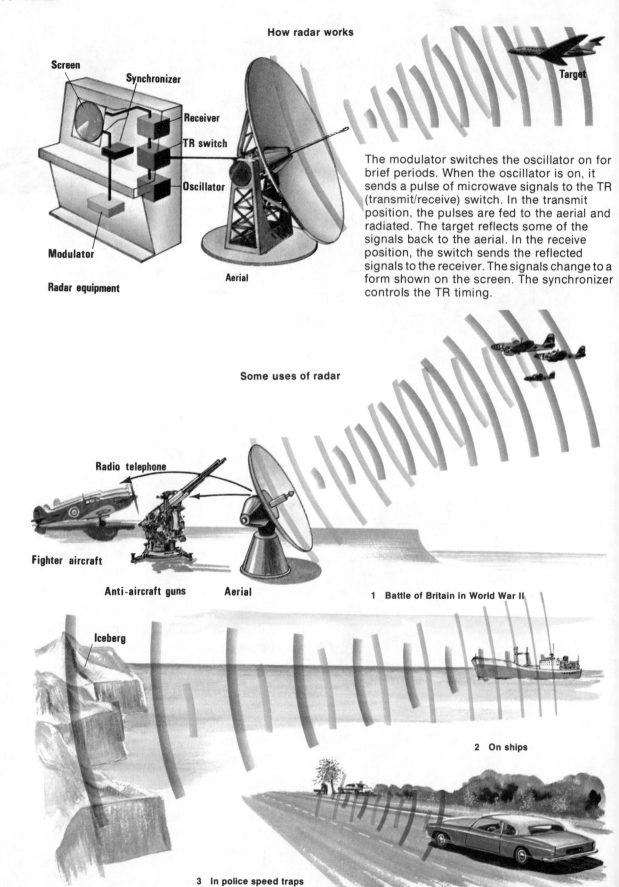

How radar works

Screen

Synchronizer

Receiver

TR switch

Oscillator

Modulator

Radar equipment

Aerial

Target

The modulator switches the oscillator on for brief periods. When the oscillator is on, it sends a pulse of microwave signals to the TR (transmit/receive) switch. In the transmit position, the pulses are fed to the aerial and radiated. The target reflects some of the signals back to the aerial. In the receive position, the switch sends the reflected signals to the receiver. The signals change to a form shown on the screen. The synchronizer controls the TR timing.

Some uses of radar

Radio telephone

Fighter aircraft

Anti-aircraft guns

Aerial

1   Battle of Britain in World War II

Iceberg

2   On ships

3   In police speed traps

show the distance of the object. The further away the object is, the further away the spot is from the center of the screen. Another kind of indicator is the range height indicator, or RHI. It shows the distance of the object and also its height.

A very different kind of radar is the continuous wave radar. In this system, the radio waves are given out continuously and not in pulses. It uses the Doppler effect to follow moving objects. (*See* DOPPLER EFFECT.) In a continuous wave radar, the frequency of the echo depends on the speed of the object. It also depends on whether the object is moving toward or away from the radar set.

The uses of radar   A very important use for radar is in navigation. Radar is used for navigating both at sea and in the air. It is particularly useful because it can be used at night and in fog. Light cannot pass through thick fog, but radio waves can. Radar is also used in airports for air-traffic control. (*See* AIRPORT.) Harbors also use radar for a similar purpose. Radars help ships to continue sailing even when the visibility is bad.

Another system used in aviation is called secondary radar. An aircraft is fitted with a device called a responder. When a radar beam hits the aircraft, the responder sends out a radio signal. The signal has a different frequency from that of the radar beam. The radar set picks up the signal from the responder. This allows the radar operator to pick out the aircraft from others around it. A similar system is used in military aircraft and ships where it is used for identifying friend from enemy. Aircraft also use radar to spot thunderclouds. Thunderclouds are dangerous to aircraft because they can cause violent disturbances. Radar can pick up thunderclouds 80 km [50 mi] away. In the same way, weathermen use radar to detect thunderclouds and hurricanes. A radar can tell the difference between the small raindrops of an ordinary cloud and the large drops of a thundercloud.

Radar also has many other uses. The police use radar to detect speeding motorists. Radar can measure the speed of a vehicle, whether it is coming or going, and whether the radar is stationary or on a moving police car. It is also used for studying the migration of birds.

M.E./L.L.R.

RADIATION (rād′ ē ā′ shən) Radiation is any flow of particles or waves from a source. Light, X rays, sound, and radio waves are forms of radiation. (*See* ELECTROMAGNETIC RADIATION.) Another example is the radiation given off by radioactive substances. There are three kinds of radiation that can be given off—alpha, beta, and gamma rays. Alpha and beta rays consist of streams of particles. Gamma rays are a very energetic form of X ray. This kind of radiation can be particularly dangerous to life. It can produce radiation sickness if a person is exposed to it for too long. (*See* RADIOACTIVITY.)   M.E./J.T.

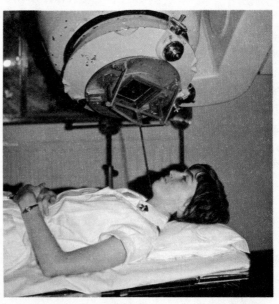

Overexposure to certain types of radiation can cause radiation sickness. However, in small doses radiation treatments can be used beneficially in medical treatments.

RADICAL (rad′ i kəl) A radical is a group of atoms in a molecule that usually is not affected by a chemical reaction. An example is the methyl radical (CH_3-). It is found in compounds such as methanol (CH_3OH) and acetaldehyde (CH_3CHO). Another example is the phenyl radical (C_6H_5-). These two radicals are found combined together in the compound toluene ($C_6H_5 \cdot CH_3$). Usually, radicals are found combined only with other radicals or with atoms in compounds. Sometimes, however, they may be freed from a compound by a chemical reaction. They are then called free radicals. Free radicals are very reactive and quickly combine to form a compound.

M.E./A.D.

RADIO

Radio (rād' ē ō') is the process of sending invisible electrical waves from one place to another. Radio is one of our most important means of communication. It enables people to send words, music, codes, and other communication signals through the air to any part of the world. Radio is also used to communicate far into space.

Broadcasting is the most familiar form of radio. Radio broadcasts include music, news, discussions, interviews, descriptions of sports events, and advertising. People wake up to clock radios, ride to work listening to automobile radios, and spend leisure hours listening to favorite radio programs.

Radio has many other uses in addition to broadcasting. Policemen, taxicab drivers, airplane pilots, astronauts, construction workers, soldiers, sailors, and many other people use radio for quick communication. Many persons, called radio amateurs, operate shortwave radio stations in their homes as a hobby. Citizen's Band radio (CB) became very popular in the 1970s. It is a means of radio communication over short distances. Many motorists and truck drivers use it to talk with other highway travelers or with people who are in an office or at home. Most CB

transmitters broadcast for distances of fewer than 8 km [5 mi] in city areas and up to 32 km [20 mi] in rural areas. Walkie-talkies are small, portable two-way radios that may operate on Citizen Band frequencies.

How radio works Radio works by changing sounds or other signals into electromagnetic waves. These are called radio waves. They are produced by a radio transmitter and travel at 299,792 km [186,000 mi] per second through air and solid objects, such as walls. When they reach a radio receiver, the receiver changes them back into the original sounds.

In a typical radio station, the electric waves representing the sounds of the program travel over wires to a control board. The control board has many switches and dials. A technician controls the sounds being sent to the board. The technician varies the loudness (volume) of each sound. He can even blend sounds together. From the control board, the electric waves go to the transmitter.

In some stations, the transmitter is in the same room or building as the control board, and the electric waves travel over wires. However, some stations have their transmitter located far from the radio station, at the site of the transmitting antenna. The transmitting antenna is the towerlike device that actually sends the radio waves through the air. In such cases, the radio waves are carried to the transmitter by wire or by a special beam of radio waves.

The transmitter strengthens the radio waves representing the broadcast. It also produces other electric waves, called carrier waves. The carrier waves are combined with the electric waves from the broadcast to form the radio signal that is transmitted. The transmitter sends the combined waves to the antenna, a tall steel tower. It, in turn, sends the waves out into the air. Transmitting antennas are usually located in high or open areas away from buildings that might interfere with the radio waves.

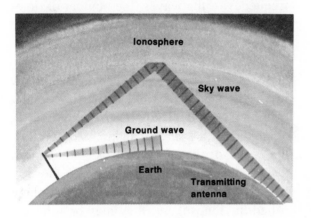

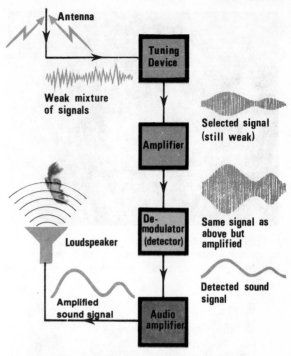

Antenna

Weak mixture
of signals

Selected signal
(still weak)

Loudspeaker

Same signal as
above but
amplified

Amplified
sound signal

Detected sound
signal

A simple TRF (tuned radio frequency) receiver.

Pentode valve

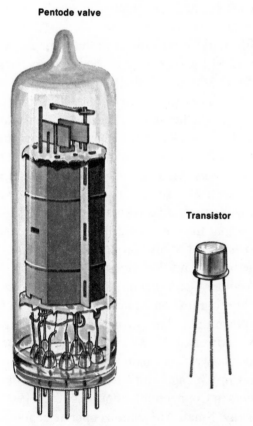

Transistor

Transistors have enabled the size of radio-wave
receivers to be reduced.

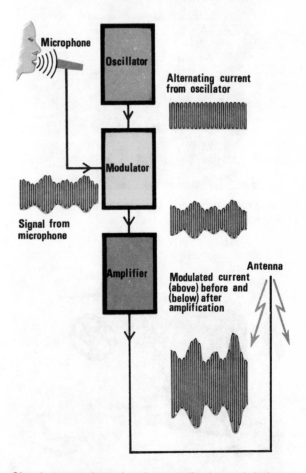

Simple transmitter showing amplitude modulation.

Guglielmo Marconi (above) developed a wireless telegraph system in the 1890s. In 1895, he transmitted radio signals over a distance of 1.61 km [1 mi]

Early radio receivers, such as the one above, were large and bulky.

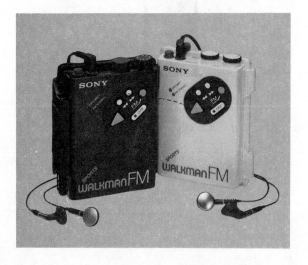

Portable stereo radios like the one left became a popular source of personal entertainment.

Radio waves Radio waves are transmitted (sent) in two ways: amplitude modulation (AM) and frequency modulation (FM). In AM transmission, the amplitude (strength) of the carrier waves varies to match changes in the electric waves coming from the radio studio. In FM transmission, the amplitude of the carrier waves remains constant. But the frequency of the waves (the number of times they vibrate each second) changes to match the electric waves sent out from the studio.

The transmitting antenna sends out two kinds of AM waves: ground waves and sky waves. Ground waves spread out horizontally from the antenna. They travel through the air along the earth's surface and may even follow the curve of the earth's surface for a short distance. Sky waves spread up into the sky. When they reach the layer of atmosphere called the ionosphere, they may be reflected back to earth. This reflection enables AM radio waves to be received at great distances from the antenna.

FM radio waves travel in the same directions as AM waves. Due to the higher carrier frequency, the waves that go skyward are not reflected. They pass through the atmosphere and go into outer space. The FM waves that travel horizontally from the antenna go in what is called line-of-sight transmission. That is, FM waves cannot be received farther than the horizon as "seen" by the antenna. FM broadcasts have an advantage over AM signals in that they are not affected by static as much as AM. FM also produces a truer reproduction of sound than does AM.

Another factor that influences the distance a radio program can be heard is the power of the transmitter. The strongest AM stations have a power of 50,000 watts. They can be heard far away. For example, a 50,000-watt station in Chicago can be heard at night by listeners in Connecticut, about 1,440 km [900 mi] away. Small AM stations operate at about

The photograph on the left shows a portable AM-FM-Short Wave stereo radio and tape player/recorder. Below is the kind of sound studio from which radio disk jockeys broadcast.

250 watts and usually serve only one or two towns. The power of FM stations ranges from 100 watts to 100,000 watts. The 100-watt stations can broadcast about 24 km [15 mi]. The 100,000-watt stations can broadcast up to 105 km [65 mi].

Each radio station operates on its own assigned channel, or frequency. This keeps stations from interfering with each other's broadcasts. Stations also have their own call letters, or names, such as WCFL (Chicago), WOR (New York), WBZ (Boston), and WWL (New Orleans). Frequency is measured in units called kilohertz and megahertz. One kilohertz equals 1,000 hertz (vibrations per second), and one megahertz equals 1 million hertz. AM stations broadcast on frequencies of between 535 and 1,605 kilohertz. The FM band extends from 88 to 108 megahertz.

Radio receivers In most instances, radio waves cannot be seen, heard, or felt. Radio receivers pick them up and change them into sounds that make up the broadcast. Some radios can receive only AM signals. Others can receive only FM signals. Still other radios can receive both signals. Some radios, including larger portable radios, can also receive shortwave, aircraft, and marine transmissions.

Almost all radios operate on electric power either from a wall outlet or a battery. The main parts of a radio are the antenna, the tuner, the amplifiers, and the loudspeaker.

The antenna is a length of wire or metal rod that picks up the radio waves. It can be entirely inside the radio, or part of it may be outside the radio but attached to it. The tuner is the device that makes it possible to pick out a particular wave, or frequency, from the many waves that strike the antenna. The frequencies are shown on a dial so that the operator knows where to position the adjusting knob. Amplifiers strengthen the signal selected by the tuner through what is called a superheterodyne circuit. The main operating

parts of this circuit in modern radios are transistors. Before the mid-1950s, however, vacuum radio tubes made of glass were used. The loudspeaker is the final link in the radio system. It changes the electric signals back into the original program sounds. (*See* LOUD-SPEAKER.)

Stereophonic radio receivers pick up stereo broadcasts from FM stations. AM stations cannot broadcast in stereo. Stereophonic receivers have at least two speakers, one each for the sounds from the right and left. This is the way they would be heard in a concert hall. This kind of radio transmission is called multiplexing.

Radio in the U.S. There are about 8,000 privately owned commercial radio stations in the U.S. There are also more than 1,100 educational stations operated by colleges and universities. Sponsors spend about three billion dollars each year in radio advertising. A station in a large city may charge about $300 for a one-minute commercial announcement. A small station may charge as little as $2 for the same message. About 40 percent of the commercial stations are affiliated with national networks such as CBS, MBS, NBC, and ABC. A network is an organization that provides some of the programing for its member stations. It also sells some of the stations' advertising time. Americans spend about three and a half billion dollars to buy 50 million radios each year. Several hundred million dollars are spent just to replace batteries in portable radios.

The Federal Communications Commission (FCC) regulates all communication by radio in the United States. It issues licenses to all radio stations and assigns frequencies and call letters. In Canada, the Canadian Broadcasting Corporation (CBC) does the same thing.

History In 1895, Guglielmo Marconi, an Italian inventor, sent the first radio signals through the air. He used electromagnetic waves to send telegraph code signals a distance of more than 1.6 km [1 mi]. In 1901, he sent code signals across the Atlantic Ocean from England to Newfoundland.

Reginald H. Fessenden, a U.S. physicist, broadcast the first human speech in 1906. He spoke from Brant Rock, Massachusetts, to ships offshore in the Atlantic Ocean. Lee De-Forest, another American inventor, produced the first experimental radio broadcast in 1910. It was broadcast from the Metropolitan Opera House in New York City and featured the famous singer, Enrico Caruso. Edwin H. Armstrong, another American, developed the superheterodyne circuit in 1918. In 1933, he discovered how to make FM broadcasts. The first commercial radio station was WWJ in Detroit. It began regular broadcasts on August 20, 1920. KDKA, a Pittsburgh station, also began in 1920. Its broadcast of the results of the presidential election on November 2, 1920 is considered by many people to be the beginning of American radio.

Broadcasting today   The advent of television in the early 1950s caused many people to speculate that the new medium would do away completely with radio. But this has not happened. The audience for radio has continued to grow. Rock music for teenagers, talk shows, call-in shows (by telephone), and increased coverage of professional sports events has helped the growth of radio. The increased availability of portable and automobile radios has also contributed to the growth. More than 17 million portable radios are sold each year. About 95 percent of all automobiles (about 104 million) have radios.   W.R.P./L.L.R.

RADIOACTIVE SERIES (rād′ ē ō ak′ tiv sir′ ēz) An atom contains a central core called a nucleus surrounded by particles called electrons. (*See* NUCLEUS, ATOMIC.) In some elements the nucleus is unstable. It gives off protons and the element changes into another element. The element is then said to be radioactive. Sometimes the element formed is itself radioactive and will decay into another element after a certain length of time. This new element may be radioactive and also decay. Eventually, the element decays to form a stable element. This series of elements is called a radioactive series.

There are three main radioactive series in nature. Two start with isotopes of uranium—uranium-235 and uranium-238. (*See* ISOTOPE.) The third starts with thorium-232. At each stage in the series the element decays. It gives off either an alpha particle or a beta particle. An alpha particle is a nucleus of helium. (*See* ALPHA PARTICLE.) When it is given off the atomic weight decreases by four. For example, thorium-232 gives off an alpha particle to form radium-228. A beta particle is an electron. (*See* BETA PARTICLE.) When it is given off, the atomic weight remains the same. But a neutron in the nucleus decays into a proton. This increases the atomic number of the element by one and it changes into another element.   M.E./A.D.

RADIOACTIVITY (rād′ ē ō ak tiv′ ət ē) Radioactivity is the property that some elements have of giving off particles and rays. All matter in the universe is made up of particles called atoms. Atoms are composed of a central core called a nucleus surrounded by tiny particles called electrons. The electron has a negative electric charge. The nucleus itself contains two kinds of particles. These are protons, with a positive charge, and neutrons, with no charge.

Different elements have different numbers of protons in their nuclei. For example, oxygen nuclei always have eight protons. However, the number of neutrons can vary and it will still be the same element. Most oxygen nuclei have eight neutrons, but a few have seven, nine, or ten neutrons. Atoms that have the same number of protons but different

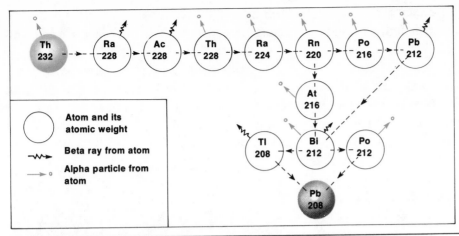

Unstable atoms
include thorium-232,
which breaks down by
a complex
process—taking
thousands of millions
of years—to lead-208.

SYMBOL	ELEMENT
Th	Thorium
Ra	Radium
Ac	Actinium
Rn	Radon
Po	Polonium
Pb	Lead
At	Astatine
Tl	Thallium
Bi	Bismuth

○ Atom and its
atomic weight

∿ Beta ray from atom

→○ Alpha particle from
atom

numbers of neutrons are called isotopes. (*See* ISOTOPE.)

As nuclei become heavier, they tend to become unstable. They break up and give off radiation. This is called radioactivity. The atoms are said to be radioactive. There are three kinds of radiation that an atom can give off. They are called alpha and beta particles and gamma rays. Alpha particles consist of two protons and two neutrons bound together. They are in fact nuclei of helium atoms. (*See* ALPHA PARTICLE.) Beta particles are electrons. They are given off when a neutron in a nucleus decays. It breaks down into a proton, an electron, and an antineutrino. The antineutrino is the antiparticle of the neutrino. (*See* NEUTRINO.) The proton stays in the nucleus but the electron and the antineutrino are ejected. (*See* BETA PARTICLE.) In both alpha and beta decay, the number of protons and neutrons in the nucleus changes. With alpha decay, there are two fewer of each particle. With beta decay, the number of protons is increased by one and the number of neutrons decreases by one. If the number of protons changes, the nucleus changes into the nucleus of another element. This process is called transmutation. (*See* TRANSMUTATION OF ELEMENTS.)

Gamma rays are very different from alpha and beta particles. They are very powerful and energetic X rays. There is no change in the number of protons or neutrons when a gamma ray is given off. The protons and neutrons in a nucleus exist in different energy levels. Those in a low level have less energy than those in a higher level. When a proton or neutron jumps from a higher level to a lower one, it loses energy. The energy is given off in the form of a gamma ray. (*See* GAMMA RAY.)

No one can tell when a radioactive nucleus will decay. But in even a small amount of matter there are millions of nuclei. After a certain length of time, half of them have decayed. This length of time is called the half life of the isotope. For example, the half life of radium-226 is 1,620 years. The half lives of other substances may be a fraction of a second or millions of years.

The radiation given off by a radioactive substance can be very dangerous to life. Special precautions have to be taken when radioactive substances are being used. The materials have to be handled by mechanical devices which are operated by remote control. Workers have to be shielded from radiation by thick lead or concrete walls. These walls must be thick enough to absorb the radiation. Strong radiation produces biological changes. These changes are often very dangerous. Sometimes, however, the changes may be for the good. Very small doses of radiation are sometimes used in medical treatments. Radia-

People working with radioactive substances have to stand behind lead glass for protection from the harmful effects of the radiation.

tion is used in curing cancer. Radioactive substances are also used in industry and in scientific research. M.E./A.D.

RADIO ASTRONOMY (rā′ dē ō ə strän′ ə mē) Radio astronomy uses radio waves to investigate the universe. Ordinary astronomy has telescopes to detect light coming from sources such as stars. Radio astronomy uses large radio telescopes to pick up radio waves coming from outer space. These radio waves are produced by objects such as stars, including our sun, planets, and gas clouds. Radio waves have a much longer wavelength than ordinary light. (*See* FREQUENCY.) For this reason, radio telescopes are much larger than optical telescopes. (*See* RADIO TELESCOPE.)

Radio astronomy began in 1931. In that year, an American radio engineer, Karl Jansky, was investigating interference in radios. He found that faint radio noises were coming from the center of our galaxy. Then, during World War II, radar was developed. Radar also uses radio waves. (*See* RADAR.) The knowledge gained in developing radar was applied to radio astronomy.

Since then, radio astronomers have made a number of important discoveries. For instance, pulsars and quasars both give out radio waves. They were first detected by radio telescopes in the 1960s. (*See* PULSAR; QUASAR.) Radio astronomy has been used to study the planets. Measurements have been made of their temperatures, distances, and the conditions of their surfaces.

Hydrogen gas gives out radiation with various wavelengths. One type of radiation is a radio wave with a wavelength of 21 cms [8.3 in]. Radio astronomers can tune into this wavelength. This has allowed them to discover the shape of our galaxy. It has a central core of stars with several curved arms leading out. A number of other galaxies also have this shape. (*See* GALAXY.)

In 1965, radio astronomers discovered that there is a faint background radiation throughout the universe. According to the big bang theory of how the universe formed, all the matter of the universe was originally compressed into a ball, which exploded and flew outward. Most astronomers now think that the background radiation is heat left over from the explosion. (*See* COSMOLOGY.) *See also* OBSERVATORY. M.E./C.R.

Radio astronomy uses large radio telescopes (above) to pick up radio waves—produced by objects such as stars—coming from outer space.

RADIO CONTROL (rād′ ē ō′ kən trōl′) Radio control is a method of controlling machines from a distance by using radio signals. A common example is radio-controlled model aircraft and boats. The model contains a small instrument that picks up radio signals. It is called the receiver. The operator is some distance away and has a transmitter. The transmitter sends signals to the receiver in the model. When the receiver picks up a signal, an electric current is produced in it. This current then operates one of the controls in the model. The signals can carry as many as ten different commands for the controls.

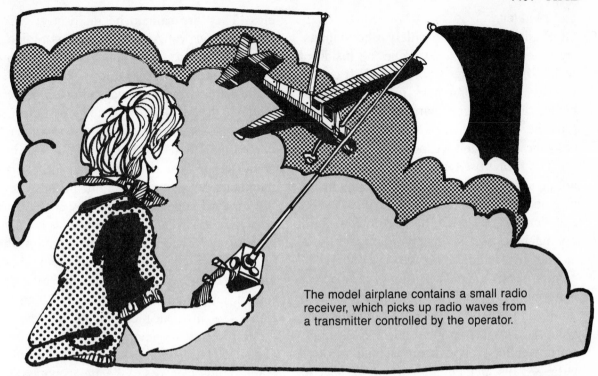

The model airplane contains a small radio receiver, which picks up radio waves from a transmitter controlled by the operator.

Radio control is used to guide probes in space exploration, missiles, and satellites. Unmanned aircraft called drones can be guided by radio signals. M.E./L.L.R.

RADIOGRAPHY (rād′ ē äg′ rə fē) Radiography is the use of penetrating radiations to make hidden structures visible. Different kinds of radiation can "see through" matter. In addition to X rays, medical radiographers use ultrasound and MRI, or magnetic resonance imaging. (*See* MEDICAL ENGINEERING.)

The science of radiography began with the discovery of X rays by Wilhelm Roentgen in 1895. The rays are used to produce images on a fluorescent screen or photographic film. The pictures produced are called radiographs. They are really shadow pictures. The densest parts of the object absorb the rays most and cast shadows. Because a radiograph is normally a transparent negative, when viewed against a light box, the densest parts show up as light areas.

Radiography has important applications in medicine. The activity of radioisotopes injected into the body is scanned by special devices, such as the positron emission tomography (PET) scanner, in order to study metabolic reactions. (*See* METABOLISM.) X rays are useful because they pass easily through the soft, fleshy parts of the body, but the denser bones cast shadows. Thus broken bones and dislocated joints show up well on a radiograph. Foreign objects such as bullets or swallowed coins are readily seen. Dental X rays reveal cavities in teeth. Chest X rays may reveal enlargement of the heart, tumors, or diseases of the lung.

Because many soft tissues and organs do not show up well, a contrast medium is used. This is a substance that is opaque to X rays (radio-opaque; it does not let radio waves through) which is introduced into the body to outline an organ or a cavity. For example, a "barium meal," a thick suspension of barium sulfate powder, may be used to show the stomach and intestines. Other radio-opaque liquids may be injected to show the flow of blood in the arteries and veins or to show the inside of the kidneys or gall bladder.

Radiography is also widely used in industry. It can be used to examine the inside of welded joints to check for defects. It can be used to search for cracks in metal components, such as aircraft parts or sections of oil pipeline. X rays can also be used to search baggage for hidden weapons.

The X rays used in medicine are normally not penetrating enough to examine the inside of metal objects. Intense rays of short wavelength are needed. Instead of using an X ray machine, as a medical radiographer does, an industrial radiographer may use a source of gamma rays. A small quantity of radioactive material in a special lead container is used to direct a beam of gamma rays through the object to a photographic plate. All high-energy radiation is dangerous, and workers with X rays and gamma rays take special precautions to avoid exposure to them. *See also* GAMMA RAYS; RADIOACTIVITY; X RAYS.

D.M.H.W./J.D.

RADIOISOTOPE (rā′ dē ō ī′ sə tōp) All matter is made up of tiny particles called atoms. At the center of the atom there is a core called the nucleus. The nucleus is made up of two types of particles: protons and neutrons. All atoms of a particular element have the same number of protons in the nucleus. For example, carbon atoms always have six protons in each nucleus. However, the number of neutrons in the nucleus can vary without changing the element. Carbon atoms usually have six neutrons in the nucleus. But some carbon atoms have seven or eight neutrons. Atoms of the same element that have different numbers of neutrons are called isotopes. (*See* ISOTOPE.) Isotopes are named after the total number of protons and neutrons in the nucleus. For example, the isotope carbon-14 contains six protons and eight neutrons in the nucleus.

Some isotopes have unstable nuclei. They break up into other nuclei and give off parti-

cles. They are said to be radioactive. (*See* RADIOACTIVITY.) An isotope that is radioactive is called a radioisotope. Some radioisotopes occur naturally. Others are made artificially. Artificial radioisotopes are made in large machines called particle accelerators. (*See* ACCELERATOR, PARTICLE.) A common method is to fire a beam of neutrons at an isotope. The neutrons are absorbed into the nuclei of the isotope. Some of these neutrons may change into a proton by giving off a small particle called an electron. This is called beta decay. Since it has gained a proton, the nucleus has changed into the nucleus of another element. Sometimes, the neutrons remain unchanged in the nuclei. In both instances, a different radioisotope is formed.

Radioisotopes have many different uses. Cobalt-60 is used to burn out cancer growths. Natural radioisotopes of the metals potassium and uranium are used to find out the age of rocks. Carbon-14 is used in a similar way to date dead material such as bones. This is called radioactive dating.

Artificial radioisotopes are used to follow the course of chemical reactions. A small amount of the radioisotope is included with a stable isotope in a compound. The compound is then reacted with another compound. The amount of radioactivity is measured in each of the products formed. This tells a scientist how the element is distributed among the products.

Radioisotopes are also used to follow the movements of compounds in plants and animals. This is called radioactive tracing. Small amounts of the radioisotope are placed in the food or injected into the organism. The movement of the radioisotope can be followed by its radiation. The concentration of the compound can also be discovered in this way.

Most substances absorb radiation. The amount absorbed depends on the thickness of the substance. This effect is used in industry to measure and control the thickness of manufactured articles.

M.E./A.D.

RADIOLARIAN (rād′ ē ō lar′ ē ən) A radiolarian is a tiny marine protozoan, similar to an ameba, except for having a delicate, glasslike skeleton made of silica. The skeleton usually forms an intricate network with numerous spines projecting from it. Radiolarians measure about 0.5 mm [0.20 in] in diameter.

The animal consists of a central capsule containing the nucleus, surrounded by a layer of frothy cytoplasm. Tiny strands extend from this outer layer to trap organisms.

The frothy protoplasm also contains tiny plants living in symbiosis with the radiolarian. When radiolarians die, their skeletons sink to the ocean floor. Large areas of the deep sea are covered with a layer of this radiolarian ooze. *See also* AMEBA; PROTOZOA; SYMBIOSIS: W.R.P./C.S.H.

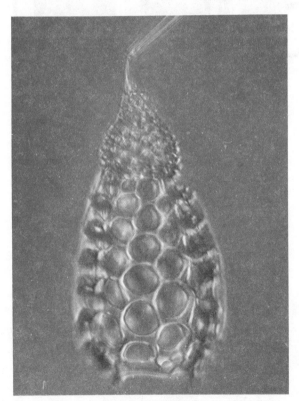

A non-spherical radiolarian is shown above. The skeleton of a radiolarian usually forms an intricate network with spines projecting from it.

RADIOLOGY (rād′ ē äl′ ə jē) Radiology is the science of the use of high-energy radiation, such as X rays and gamma rays, particularly in medicine. Radiation may be used to diagnose disease. (*See* RADIOGRAPHY.) It may also be used to treat disease. (*See* RADIOTHERAPY.) Both of these studies are branches of radiology.   D.M.H.W./A.I.

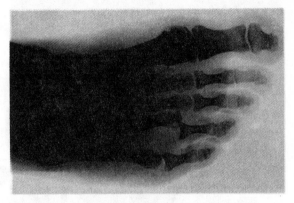

This X-ray photograph shows a foot dislocation.

RADIOSONDE (rād′ ē ō sänd′) A radiosonde is a device that takes measurements in the upper atmosphere. A radiosonde consists of meteorological (weather science) instruments carried into the atmosphere by a helium or hydrogen balloon. The instruments aboard the radiosonde record the temperature, dew point, humidity, barometric (atmospheric) pressure, and wind speed and direction at various heights above the earth. The data obtained is sent by radio back to weather stations on the earth. The measurements taken by a radiosonde are called soundings.

Meteorologists can determine the state of the jet stream by using radiosondes. The information about the jet stream is used to predict the formation and movements of storms and other weather systems. (*See* JET STREAM.) Radiosondes also send data that can be used to determine the stability of the atmosphere. If the atmosphere is very stable, a meteorologist may predict high air pollution levels. If the atmosphere is very unstable, a meteorologist may predict thunderstorms and, possibly, tornadoes. *See also* METEOROLOGY; THUNDERSTORM; WEATHER.   J.M.C./C.R.

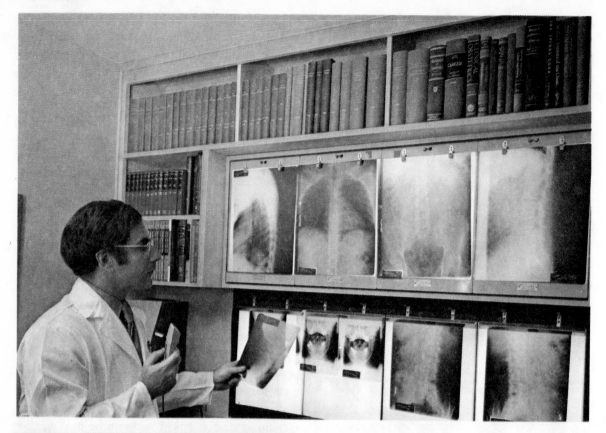

A radiologist (above) examines X-ray photographs, also known as radiographs.

RADIO TELESCOPE (rād′ ē ō′ tel′ ə skōp′) Radio astronomy is the branch of astronomy that uses radio waves to study the universe. Many objects in outer space give out radio waves just as they give out light waves. The light waves are detected by optical telescopes. The radio waves are detected by using an instrument called a radio telescope.

The radio waves are picked up by the part of the telescope called the antenna. The antenna is tuned to pick up radio waves of a particular wavelength. (*See* FREQUENCY.) In this, it is similar to a domestic radio that is tuned to a particular station. Many radio telescopes have just one antenna. Others have two that are spaced some distance apart. Both antennas are pointed at the same source of

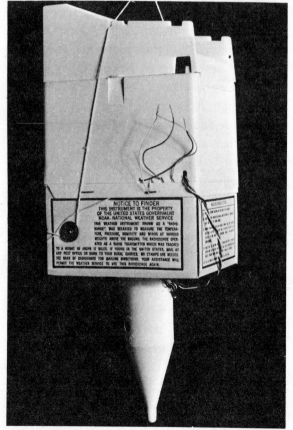

Shown at the left is a National Weather Service radiosonde. Note the instructions on how to return the instrument to the government.

radio waves. The signals they receive are combined. This is called interference. It tells the astronomer more about the source than just one antenna would. (*See* INTERFERENCE.)

Radio telescopes may have several antennas. They are arranged in a circle or in a cross. They allow the telescope to pick up even more details about the source. Bigger radio telescopes have lines of antennas that may stretch for several miles.

Radio telescopes are not used only for picking up signals. They can also be used like a radar set. They can beam radio waves at the moon or at a planet and detect the reflected signal. Using this method, radio astronomers have made a simple map of the planet Venus. The surface of Venus is hidden from optical telescopes by a thick bank of cloud. Light cannot pass through this cloud, but radio waves can.

Radio waves from outer space were first discovered by the American radio engineer Karl Jansky in 1931. Six years later, the first radio telescope was built by an American amateur, Grote Reber. For many years, the biggest radio telescope in the world was at Jodrell Bank in England. It had a dish-shaped antenna 75 m [250 ft] across. In the early 1960s, American scientists built a bigger telescope in a mountain hollow in Puerto Rico. It is 300 m [1,000 ft] across. This telescope cannot be steered. Different parts of the sky are observed by moving the antennas to different parts of the dish. A similar telescope with an antenna 600 m [2,000 ft] across has now been built in the U.S.S.R. *See also* RADIO ASTRONOMY. M.E./C.R.

RADIOTHERAPY (rād′ ē ō ther′ ə pē) Radiotherapy is the use of radiation to cure disease. The radiation used is very high-energy radiation—X rays and gamma rays. (*See* ELECTROMAGNETIC RADIATION.) These rays are very penetrating. In large doses the rays are very destructive. They damage and destroy living cells. However, this destructive

effect can sometimes be put to good use. By carefully calculating the dosage of radiation, a radiotherapist can destroy unwanted cells without damaging healthy tissues too much.

Radiation has its greatest effect on cells that are dividing to produce new cells. In cancer, the cells of a tissue grow and divide more than normal. They are "runaway" cells, not controlled by the body. They grow and produce unnatural swellings, or tumors, in different parts of the body. If the rapidly-dividing cells are killed, cancer may be slowed down or completely stopped.

To destroy a cancer, a beam of high-energy X rays is focused on it. Alternatively, a beam of gamma rays may be used. The gamma rays are directed from a quantity of radioactive substance, such as radiocobalt, in a special shielded container with a small aperture. Sometimes a radioactive pellet or radioactive needles may be inserted into the tumor. In some cases a patient may be given an injection of a radioisotope that becomes concentrated in a particular body tissue. Cancer of the thyroid gland may be treated in this way with radioactive iodine compounds. *See also* GAMMA RAY; RADIOACTIVITY; RADIOISOTOPE; X RAY. D.M.H.W./A.I.

RADISH (rad′ ish) The radish is an annual plant of the mustard family Cruciferae. It is grown widely for its edible root, which is used as an appetizer and in salads. There are many different kinds of radishes. The most common variety grown in the United States is the spring radish.

The roots vary in shape, size, and color depending upon the variety. The United States variety is generally round in shape with a bright red skin. The flesh is white and firm, and somewhat like that of a potato. It has a distinctive sharp taste.

Radishes grow throughout the year in mild, cool climates. In Japan and China, people grow a winter radish, called a daikon. W.R.P./F.W.S.

RADIUM (rād′ ē əm) Radium (Ra) is a radioactive white metallic element. Its atomic number is 88 and its atomic weight is 226.026. It melts at 700°C [1,290°F] and boils at 1,140°C [2,080°F]. Its relative density is about 5.

Radium was discovered in 1898 by the French chemists Marie and Pierre Curie. (*See* CURIE FAMILY.) It occurs in very small amounts in uranium ores such as pitchblende. It is used in medicine to destroy cancer growths. However, it has to be handled very carefully as it can cause bad radiation burns. There are 13 isotopes of radium. (*See* ISOTOPE.) The most common is radium-226. Its half life is 1,620 years. *See also* RADIOACTIVITY.   M.E./J.R.W.

RADIUS (rād′ ē əs) In anatomy, the radius is the bone of the forearm on the thumb side. In human beings, the radius is shorter than the other bone of the forearm, called the ulna. The radius moves around and crosses the ulna as the hand is turned to cause the palm to face backward. All land vertebrates have this bone.

In the geometry of a circle or a sphere, the radius is the distance from the center to any point on the circumference or surface. (*See* GEOMETRY.)   J.J.A./J.J.F.

RADON (rā′ dän′) Radon (Rn) is a radioactive gas. It is one of the noble gases. (*See* NOBLE GAS.) Its atomic number is 86. Radon liquefies at −61.8°C [−79.2°F] and becomes solid at −71°C [−96°F].

Radon was discovered in 1900 by the German scientist Friedrich Dorn. He found that the gas is given off when the metal radium decays. Because it soon decays into other elements radon occurs only in very small amounts. There are 20 isotopes of radon. The longest-lived is radon-222. Its half life is just under three days. Radon is used in medical treatments for cancer.

In 1985, U.S. public health officials warned that many homes in the area extending from eastern Pennsylvania through New Jersey to New York may be contaminated with radon originating from radium in natural uranium deposits underlying these homes. Radon levels were reported to be high enough, in some instances, to cause an increased risk of lung cancer.   M.E./J.R.W.

Pierre and Marie Curie in their laboratory, where they discovered radium.   ©The Bettmann Archive, Inc.

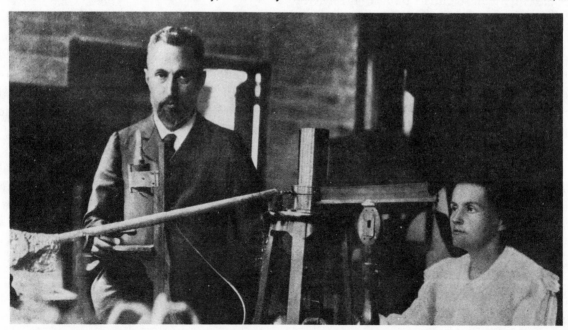